OPERATIONS RESEARCH:
IMPLICATIONS FOR LIBRARIES

Thanks are tendered to the Joseph Fels Foundation, Inc., for financial support of the Conference from which these Proceedings come.

OPERATIONS RESEARCH: IMPLICATIONS FOR LIBRARIES

The Thirty-fifth Annual Conference
of the Graduate Library School
August 2–4, 1971

Edited by DON R. SWANSON
and ABRAHAM BOOKSTEIN

THE UNIVERSITY OF CHICAGO PRESS
CHICAGO & LONDON

THE UNIVERSITY OF CHICAGO STUDIES IN LIBRARY SCIENCE

The papers in this volume were published originally in the

LIBRARY QUARTERLY, *January 1972*

Standard Book Number: 0-226-78466-5
Library of Congress Catalog Card Number: 73-186760

THE UNIVERSITY OF CHICAGO PRESS, CHICAGO AND LONDON

TABLE OF CONTENTS

OPERATIONS RESEARCH: IMPLICATIONS FOR LIBRARIES

INTRODUCTION

ABRAHAM BOOKSTEIN AND DON R. SWANSON

Library operations in recent times have been characterized by a great increase in complexity. The rapid expansion of collections, both in size and scope, the great variety of forms taken by items that now must be housed in the library, and the growth in expectations among library users are among the factors that have contributed to this complexity. In this setting, managerial decision making in the library has become an unenviably difficult task. Furthermore, the new technologies and new techniques which offer great opportunities for library planners and managers make even more difficult the use of traditional, intuitive approaches. It is reasonable to ask whether techniques such as Operations Research (O. R.) that have proved valuable in similar situations for business and government, might not also be of service in libraries.

Although many definitions of Operations Research are given in the literature, the enormous variety of problems to which O. R. has been applied suggest that rigid boundaries between what is and what is not O. R. should not be drawn. Philip Morse, one of the pioneers of this field, has defined O. R. as "a scientific method of providing executive departments with a quantitative basis for decisions regarding the operations under their control" [1, p. 1]. More loosely, Richard Bellman once said that it is really no more than a "state of mind"; such a definition, it must be admitted, is hard to argue with.

Examined in retrospect, O. R. can usefully be thought of in terms of a confluence of two major developments in the management of complex organizations: the Scientific Management[1] movement in industry and the use of teams of scientists for solving military problems.

The first of these developments, whose origin is generally attributed to the work of Fredrich Taylor [2], attempts to improve the effectiveness of an organization by studying its operations in detail and eliminating those inefficiencies that are discovered. The measurement of times and motions required for operations is a characteristic of this approach. The importance of the Scientific Management school lies in its

[1] This term should not be confused with "Management Science," which is essentially the same as "Operations Research."

1

recognition that business procedures can be subject to systematic or quantitative examination and in its approach of carefully analyzing complex operations into components that can be easily studied. The willingness to examine, and even modify, traditional procedures is the major claim of Scientific Management; discussions of successful applications exist in library [3] as well as business literature. A major weakness of this school is the absence of analytic techniques that can form the basis of a deeper understanding of the processes involved and that would allow a fuller exploitation of its methodology. As the field merged with "Operations Research," "Management Science," and the "System Approach"—all of which came to mean pretty much the same thing—this weakness was largely remedied.

Operations Research, as a profession and as an organized activity, originated in England at the beginning of World War II.[2] The term was used to describe the activities of scientists and mathematicians in formulating and solving problems related to military operations. These scientists naturally used approaches with which they were most familiar: they developed models that abstracted those features from rather complex situations that were most relevant to finding a solution; they experimented to test the validity of their models; and they used (and developed) mathematical techniques to draw conclusions from their models. It is this approach—involving the use of interdisciplinary teams, the creation of mathematical models, and guidance by the

methodology of science—that at the end of the war merged with scientific management and provided it with an analytic edge as well as with a more sophisticated philosophy and methodology. There can be little doubt that the allied military operations of World War II provided a major impetus for Operations Research as a profession; O. R. activities spread into business and industry following World War II as rapidly as it did principally because of the large numbers of experienced scientists who had become acquainted with and interested in military operational problems during the war.

Operations Research has developed rapidly since its origins in World War II. Organizations such as the Operational Research Society (in Britain) and the Operations Research Society of America were formed to facilitate communications among workers in this field. As its techniques became more elaborate, a number of universities began programs in this subject; some of these techniques have virtually become separate disciplines in their own right. Practitioners of O. R. have contributed to almost every aspect of government and business. More recently, a number of operations researchers have turned their attention to library and information systems, and we believe significant research has resulted.

It is the purpose of this conference to introduce the library audience to some of these accomplishments. Although Operations Research in libraries is still a very young endeavor, with many of its characteristics yet to be developed, we believe that these papers do offer sufficient insights into the nature of an O. R. approach to libraries so as to make their presentation of value to librarians. Both the methodol-

---

[2] A more detailed account of the early history of O. R., principally dealing with the period 1939–52, may be found in the first chapter of reference [4].

ogy and the tools of O. R. are described; it is these that O. R. offers to a library manager. Combined with library experience, sensitivity to library needs, and a willingness to modify traditional operations, O. R. has great potential for assisting library management. For this potential to be realized, however, it will be necessary for librarians to involve themselves more intensively with this research and provide it with professional guidance. It is hoped that the nature of the effort required may become clearer because of this conference. We also hope it will make clearer the relation between Operations Research and other aspects of library management: it will suggest the power and scope of O. R., but it will also emphasize that O. R. can assist but not replace either managerial judgment or extensive library experience.

This conference does not presume to define the limits of Operations Research in the field of librarianship. Rather, an attempt was made in organizing this conference to select representative and important lines of substantive work and to invite those who have carried out this work to prepare papers addressed to a library audience. These papers can be divided into two groups. The first group emphasizes the theoretical and philosophical aspects of O. R. Among these is the introductory paper by West Churchman which presents an overview of O. R., describing its methodology, its limitations as it is currently being practiced, and its potentials. This philosophical discussion is continued by F. Leimkuhler, who views O. R. as the product of a society in rapid transition.

The heart of a formal O. R. study is the creation of abstract models that represent the environment being studied. Leimkuhler illustrates these by de-

scribing storage models created in the course of his own research in libraries. The papers by Morse, Korfhage, and Kochen further illustrate how O. R. models can be used to describe a real situation and why such models are of value. Many of these models involve relatively elementary mathematics and should be comprehensible to the non-mathematician willing to devote a reasonable amount of effort. To create these models demanded an ingenious application of the appropriate, though possibly elementary, mathematics to problem situations more than an ability to use sophisticated techniques. It is likely that, in the course of actual library management, most O. R. applications will be of such a nature.

As the interests of operations researchers extended to increasing numbers of organizations, it was found that a number of abstract models frequently recurred. These models were singled out for special attention. Their theoretical properties were studied, solution techniques were refined, and their scope generalized—this work often being carried out by mathematicians more attracted by the challenge of the model than by its application to any specific situation. This kind of research has enhanced the intellectual appreciation of these models and has provided new techniques that can increase their value for practical application.

One such technique is linear programming [5]; a linear-programming problem essentially asks how a function having a given form can be made as large as possible by adjusting its variables among a restricted set of values. It is possible today to solve very large problems of this kind. If we further demand that the variables assume only integral values, the problem becomes considerably more difficult to solve; however, such a restriction can also make the model much more powerful. For example, by restricting the values to be zero or one, the model can represent decisions as to which among a very large number of alternatives we should do. In the paper by Glover, these are decisions as to whether or not we should buy a particular issue of a given journal and, if so, in which year subsequent to its publication. Here, the function that is to be maximized is the total expected amount of journal use, dependent upon which journal issues are bought and when they are bought. The constraints prevent issues of journals from being bought more than once and keep expenditures within budgetary limitations; consideration is given to expenses in a given year due to journal issues previously purchased. Glover presents a theoretical analysis of this problem and gives techniques by means of which problems of this type can be solved; the emphasis is on the theoretical analysis of this model rather than on its justification.

The second group of papers considers problems more oriented toward applications than toward theoretical models. Buckland describes how the University of Lancaster library used O. R. techniques to create a more flexible circulation policy which resulted in improving the availability of library materials. The papers by Ramist and by Lipetz indicate how data that may prove valuable for the analysis of a library's operations could be gathered. Ramist suggests some models for fund allocation and describes techniques he used to collect the data called for by these models; in this manner he was able to produce a measure of effectiveness for a large public library system. Lipetz pre-

sents extensive data on catalog use and treats substantively the problems of experimental design in gathering such data. The conference concludes with a paper by Bookstein which considers the nature of an education for library O. R. workers and discusses some difficulties involved in introducing such a program into a library school's curriculum.

Not all work relevant to library operations research is explicitly so labeled; indeed, it is not easy to define what is meant by relevance in this context. Some idea of the scope of the subject can be obtained from the bibliographies attached to the various papers presented in this volume and from the separate bibliography compiled by V. Slamecka (p. 152). Slamecka worked independently of the authors participating in this conference and produced a selected bibliography of 153 items. A composite bibliography of references carried by the papers of this conference would consist of about 125 items. It is noteworthy that there are only about sixteen references in common between the latter 125 and Slamecka's 153. Neither bibliography was intended as comprehensive, and, since they were selected with different criteria in mind, the small amount of overlap is not surprising. Yet, in some sense, each must represent just a portion of a much larger field. If we view this larger field in a broad sense as containing everything related to library operations research, it is clear that it would probably include many hundreds of papers on a great variety of topics neither mentioned in this conference nor included in its bibliographies.

The papers in this volume seem to share at least one attribute with nearly all operations research, namely, the quest for an optimum, whether it is for network design, directory design, library use, journal use, the number of copies of a book, the loan period for a book, or simply cost. The thoughtful reader may notice that too often, perhaps, it is only the *quantity* (for example, circulation, etc.) of library use that is taken as a measure of something to be optimized, without regard to the quality or nature of such use. It must be admitted that the latter is most difficult to grasp in measurable terms, so perhaps the failure to do so is forgivable.

Although our authors had been exhorted to keep mathematical demands on their readers to a minimum, they did not all succeed to the same degree. Librarians attempting to cope with some of these papers are likely to notice that there is a communication gap of significant dimensions between themselves and operations researchers. The native speaker of English does not always communicate easily with the native speaker of mathematics, and each, we hope, will be tolerant of the other and extend himself to a reasonable degree.

Many readers may feel much like Charlie Brown after Lucy asked him why he didn't like mathematics, since, after all, she says, "it is a very precise subject." Charlie replied, "That's just the trouble, I'm at my best in something where the answers are mostly a matter of opinion." Charlie, we see, has captured neatly, if indirectly, the spirit of Operations Research, for certainly its aim is to provide some basis for operational decisions other than opinion or tradition.

REFERENCES

1. Morse, Philip M., and Kimball, George E. *Methods of Operations Research*. New York: John Wiley & Sons, 1951.
2. Etzioni, Amitai. *Modern Organizations*. Englewood Cliffs, N.J.: Prentice-Hall, Inc., 1964.
3. Shaw, Ralph R. "Scientific Management in the Library." *Wilson Library Bulletin* 21 (January 1947): 349–52.
4. McCloskey, Joseph E., and Trefethen, Florence W., eds. *Operations Research for Management*. Baltimore: Johns Hopkins Press, 1954.
5. Danzig, George Bernard. *Linear Programming and Extensions*. Princeton, N.J.: Princeton University Press, 1963.

OPERATIONS RESEARCH PROSPECTS FOR LIBRARIES: THE REALITIES AND IDEALS

C. WEST CHURCHMAN

ABSTRACT

Operations research can be described in terms of a specific strategy of research. The purpose of this paper is to describe and criticize a very common strategy in which the operations researcher relies strongly on managerial judgment and the existing system as a basis for his inquiry. In this strategy, the operations researcher takes the libraries and specifically the user behavior as givens and relies heavily on library administrators as a basis for his models and his data. The current strategy is criticized in idealistic terms. It may very well be that operations researchers are solving the wrong problems because the existing system—for example, the library—may itself be seriously faulty in its design with respect to the real clients.

The aim of this paper is quite broad: to discuss operations research in terms of its strategies. That is to say, we are going to regard operations research as an "inquiring system" [1] with special relevance to libraries. Operations research is a system of inquiry with its own resources, components, and environment and with the primary purpose of generating recommendations to managers for changing their systems to improve them. To avoid confusion, it will be important to note that I will talk about how operations researchers study systems and about operations research as an inquiring system. It should also be noted that there are many labels like operations research, for example, systems science, systems analysis, and management science, and that for the purpose of this paper all of these are subsumed under what might be called the systems approach [2].

The topic of the paper falls into two parts, which I call the realistic and the idealistic. The realistic part attempts to look at operations research just as the operations researcher normally looks at any real system, namely, how the system operates at the present time. The idealistic section, on the other hand, attempts to raise questions as to how the system called operations research ought to be designed.

To begin with the realistic part, we can identify the chief resources of operations research as follows:

First, there is a *logic* of values, that is, a way of looking at systems in terms of a specific set of purposes which hopefully can be expressed in quantitative terms subject to certain constraints. For example, in operations research we often think of the primary purpose of a system as one of cost minimization subject to a specified service level. Thus, one might ask how to operate the cataloging component of a library subject to some policy which limits the time between the receipt of a document and its recording in the library catalog in such a way as to minimize the cost of the cataloging operation. Alternatively, the values might take the form of minimizing the waiting time of the clients of the system subject to budget limitations, as one might try to do for the check-out desk of the library. The waiting-line problem displays the well-known conflict of values. The larger the budget, the easier it is to treat the waiting-line problem; but on the other hand, a large number of people working at the check-out desk amounts to a great deal of idle service time. The operations research task, therefore, is one of minimizing waiting time subject to certain policies regarding idle time, policies that are largely conditioned by budgetary constraints.

Alternatively, one might try to maximize the total "benefit" minus "cost" subject to policy stipulations, where benefit and cost are represented as economic measures and policy stipulations arise from various kinds of legal, moral, and managerial considerations.

We may note in passing that the logic of values as used by the operations researchers is a fairly sophisticated one. For example, the policy constraints on the system can be translated into cost or benefit measures. This is why all the recent excitement about "social indicators" [3] seems to the operations researcher to be irrelevant, since he has always included social values in his analysis. But a further exploration into the logic of operations research would not really serve a useful purpose here.

In addition to his logic, the operations researcher has at his disposal a tool kit of models and computer simulation techniques, plus a kind of open-ended mode of representing problems which is not limited by the existing models. A recent book by Harvey Wagner entitled *Principles of Operations Research* [4] illustrates very well what this tool kit of models looks like. In his book, Wagner reviews in

elementary form the enormous developments of the last two decades, in which applied mathematicians have worked out a large library of operations research models: mathematical programming, dynamic programming, inventory, waiting line, etc. Not mentioned in Wagner's book, but still attractive to some, is the work of Jay Forrester. Forrester's work now stretches from industrial dynamics (1961) [5], through urban dynamics (1969) [6], to world dynamics (1971) [7].

These are essentially the conceptual resources of the operations researcher. His support systems are the following: (1) existing data banks associated with the systems he studies: accounting and other cost data, past-demand records, etc.; (2) managerial and other expert judgments, used to ascertain the purposes of the system, its policies, the system boundaries, the characteristics of the environment of the system, and, most important of all, the critical problems that the system faces; and (3) perhaps the funding support system, which is the most important of the support systems from a survival point of view.

From these considerations of the conceptual resources and the support systems, the commonly adopted strategy of operations research has emerged. The strategy consists of the following:

1. In the main, the operations researcher accepts the system as it is defined by the managers. For example, an operations researcher would typically accept the fact that a library is a system which is a part of a larger system, for example, a university or a city. The operations researcher also accepts the manager's judgment as to the clientele whom the system should

be serving. In the case of libraries, the clientele would normally be a subclass of the population. The operations researcher goes on to accept the manager's judgment about how the potential clientele is to be classified in terms of individual needs, the right to obtain documents, and other related information. Finally, the operations researcher will generally accept the management's judgment as to the basic purposes of the library system, but of course operations research may help to clarify the purposes as it moves toward quantitative measures of performance. He does not expect management to provide him with a quantitative measure of performance, but he does expect that sufficient information will be supplied by management so that an appropriate measure will emerge. For example, the management of a library may explain to an operations researcher that the library system exists for the purpose of making a certain class of information available to a specific client at a minimum cost.

2. Usually the operations researcher also accepts either the traditional or the current managerial judgment concerning the system components. Typically, the system components are derived from an organization chart of the system. For example, judging from the papers of this conference, the operations researchers would see the library as a system with components such as a journal subscription department, storage department, loan department, finance department, catalog department, etc.

3. Normally the operations researcher spends the first part of the study trying to understand the system as defined by 1 and 2 above. With the help of managerial judgment, he then proceeds to try to understand which component has really critical problems. He is anxious to identify those problems where the *net* payoff from operations research will be greatest. It is to be noted that this and the next step are not well defined as a strategy and are often the greatest pitfalls of operations research.

4. Once the operations researcher has identified some of the critical problems of the system components, he then tries to match the critical problem with his chief conceptual resources, the logic and especially the models mentioned above. But, if he is a wise operations researcher, he also has to pay considerable attention to available data banks and available managerial judgment.

The pitfall alluded to above arises because the operations researcher, in his enthusiasm about the fit between a critical problem and one of his models, may come to believe that, provided there is adequate funding, the fit is all that's really needed to enable him to decide on the problem that should be tackled. For example, in observing libraries he will certainly see that the library is faced with a good deal of what is called "waiting line" problems. The arrival of books to be cataloged and the arrival of people at the checkout counter are two rather prominent examples. In both cases, the intellectually well-trained operations researcher sees right away that he may be able to apply the techniques of waiting-line analysis. He therefore may decide right away to collect information on the way the books come in or the clients arrive for service. He would then expect to try to develop the probability of arrival and allied information that is essential in waiting-line analysis. In his enthusiasm he may believe that one of his models matching the critical problem of the library (and certainly, cataloging and service of the clients at the counter are critical problems in all libraries) is enough for him to get started. But there is also a more basic concern, namely, the ability of the operations researcher to implement the findings. The operations researcher is apt to rush in where the problem fits the model but where management is not about to change the system, or certainly not to change it in the way in which the operations researcher would recommend. Often, managerial resistance to change is based on the politics of the system, for example, fear of losing personnel or other forms of power within the organization. If you reflect on the matter, you will easily see that making waiting-line systems operate more efficiently may very well result in firing individuals or in reallocating them within the organization, changes that various members of management may strongly resist.

It is important to note that these two last steps, the identification of the critical problems and the decision as to where operations research can be helpful, are themselves systems decisions, very much like any of the decisions that the operations researcher himself studies. In making the decision as to what problem he should work on, the operations researcher is in effect making a managerial judgment that working on some particular problem is a better use of resources than any other alternative use. Indeed, if he were to apply his own logic, which I mentioned above in discussing the intellectual resources of operations research, he would have to see that the judgment about which problem to work on is a

judgment about maximizing some value subject to certain constraints, which may be political constraints. Like most disciplines (for example, psychology, philosophy, and economics), operations research has its own self-reflective part. The operations research inquiring system has an operations research problem to solve.

It is to be noted that the literature of operations research rarely mentions this very critical aspect, perhaps because the operations researcher himself knows very little about it (but see [8]). In my experience, operations researchers often use rather trivial reasons for not tackling certain problems; for example, the problem is "not feasible." The phrase "not feasible" literally means "cannot practically be done," so that all that the judgment consists of is simply saying, in a somewhat arbitrary way, that the problem cannot be tackled. Words are curious things. If I say that a certain task is impossible, I may arouse the spirit of the hero to conquer the unconquerable, but if I say that it is not feasible, no one is apt to object.

The main point to be made is that the operations researcher is trying through his research to maximize some return, for example, economic gain, by changing the character of the system subject to certain constraints, of which the time span of the research is a very important one. Operations research studies can be done, say, in ten weeks, but the "solution" of such studies is quite different from the "solution" of a study which is budgeted to run for two years. Mere absence of data does not necessarily mean that the operations researcher is stymied. If he is honest, he realizes that almost all of the data he uses are subject to suspicion and that he very frequently fills in data gaps by means of judgment, guesses, and so on.

5. The next step of the operations research inquiring system is to gather the data and the managerial judgments to "fill in" the model, that is, to make the model "realistic." In my experience, this part of the operations research effort consumes up to 95 percent of the total amount of effort. It is by far the most frustrating part, as I have already mentioned, because the operations researcher is pretty much on his own in deciding which data to use and which judgments to rely upon.

I can illustrate this point by one brief example. In the textbooks on operations research, the student is told that, wherever a problem includes a certain kind of demand from the clientele, he should look in the past records to see how the client has behaved. But even if the records are available, past performance of the client may be totally irrelevant, especially if the opportunity exists (and it almost always does) of changing client behavior by price mechanisms, advertising, and so on. Another way to say the same thing is that to restrict library user studies to those who actually come into the library may be a mistaken approach. Perhaps the most important group of people are those who would use the library provided certain policies are changed; for example, studies of book circulation may seriously miss the mark. It has only been by a fairly slow process that we have come to realize that the linkages of one system to another (for example, in the case of the libraries, the linkage of the university library to the total educational system) are extremely critical to the way in which we regard available data.

6. Next, the operations researcher derives a recommendation, that is to say, he tries to estimate an optimal change within the system as it has been previously defined. I should emphasize that the word "next" is only used for purposes of exposition. The steps outlined in the strategy are obviously not sequential steps in time. Often an operations researcher will derive a recommendation which he decides does not make good sense. He sees that it will be necessary to go back and recast the problem. As in all science, the strategies are interlinked and repeat themselves in a self-checking manner.

The real point to be made in the recommendation-derivation part of the operations research system is that the operations researcher is making an *estimate* of the optimal. This aspect of operations research is often misunderstood and has resulted in unenlightened criticisms of operations research. For example, operations research is often accused of coming up with the "one best way." The critic points out that libraries differ, or that each library is unique and that the operations researcher is trying to apply general rules which do not work in the case of specific libraries. This, of course, is not the case. What is general about operations research is its method, which in principle it takes to be applicable to all systems. But the operations researcher tries to make a very concerted effort to understand the individual characteristics of the system he is studying, and these individual characteristics appear as the coefficients and constraints in his models.

Or, the operations researcher is often accused of trying to arrive at *the* solution, and the critic points out that "no problem has a solution." But here again, the critic has failed to understand that operations research, like all science, does not try to arrive at the final answer, since, as all scientists know, there is no "final" answer available to us except in the idealistic limit. Rather, the operations researcher regards his efforts with all the humility of any scientist, namely, that he does the best he can with the available evidence to derive an estimate of the optimal. The estimate, of course, may be wrong, and the operations researcher (as distinguished from most other advisors and consultants to organizations) often attempts to make some estimate as to how far off his recommendation may be from the true optimal by means of what is called sensitivity analysis.

Perhaps the most deceptive criticism of all is the notion that "no one tries to optimize; the sensible manager only tries to reach a satisfactory level of performance." This criticism has greatly irritated many operations researchers. It is illustrated by pointing out that, if one were looking for a very sharp needle in a haystack, he would not feel obliged to examine every possible needle; he would just look for one that was "sharp enough." To this, the operations researcher could only reply, "Of course." Every operations research study, if it is sensible, involves the cost of continued research in depth. As I pointed out above, operations research studies define "solutions" as relative to the budget and available time. No operations researcher in his right mind is claiming that his solution is the best, given that he could work forever with all of the funding in the world.

7. Finally, the operations researcher attempts to "implement" the recommendation. This is probably the least understood aspect of operations research. In practice, operations researchers'

concern about implementation ranges from merely reporting to management, to a very active, intervening role. Here, the strategies of operations research can be divided into four possibilities (see [9] for further details). First is that the operations researcher's job is to do the best he can to generate a recommendation, and then it is totally up to the management to implement the recommendation. Sometimes the operations researcher only tries to develop some informative measures which he hopes will help the manager make decisions. The paper by Philip Morse in this series is an excellent example of this strategy. Second is that the operations researcher should be engaged in trying to educate the managers about operations research and its methods, in addition to generating recommendations. The third strategy consists of saying that the operations researcher has the obligation to try to understand management more thoroughly, specifically the political, social, and moral problems of management. The fourth strategy says that, in effect, operations research and management form an ongoing team in that each relies on the other and learns from the other. At this stage in history, it would be ridiculous to say that any one of these four strategies is "optimal" for an operations research inquiring system, although certainly the last has the most appealing tone and hence reflects my personal bias.

I have tried thus far to characterize the operations research system. But I hope it is obvious enough that in a paper of this length I cannot touch on the various imaginative proceedings that many operations research teams have found to deal with the problems that they face. Many of them, of course, have not simply accepted the system they study as it is. Many of them have been deeply concerned about the method of selecting a problem to work on, the implementation of their recommendations, and so on. But the above, I feel, represents a fairly accurate general description of how operations research behaves today.

Now suppose we discuss the idealistic critique. Here we have a *challenge*— that operations research may be solving precisely the wrong problems—and the *justification of the challenge*—*because* the mode of representing the system may be wrong.

Three illustrations will be enough to set the tone of the challenge and its justification. Today we hear a great deal about health, health planning, health services, and the dangers that the nation and the world are running into with respect to health problems. Almost all of the discussion centers on the fact that available health services (hospitals, mental health clinics, etc.) are becoming more and more costly while the need for them is increasing. You will note that the discussions about health are based pretty much on the same kind of strategy I described for operations research, namely, that "health services" are to be defined in terms of the existing health system and its components—hospitals, clinics, and the like. But it is not difficult to argue that this way of representing the health problem may be far too narrow. To be sure, certain people in desperate physical condition do need certain kinds of care. But it is easy to speculate that the real problems of health have their origin in the way individuals lead their lives, and in particular in the polarization that is so obvious in the world today, of poor and rich, white and black, developers and conservationists, developed and developing nations, democratic and Communist nations, and so on. In every community of our nation the feeling of polarization between the young and the middle-aged is rampant. One might argue, therefore, that the real problem of health today is not the creation of more services but addressing the real causes of health breakdowns, namely, polarization in its many forms. If one did argue this way, then one would see that trying to operate a hospital a little more cheaply may be "solving precisely the wrong problem."

Or again, consider education. To many a legislator today, the problem of education at the undergraduate level is how we can get teachers to take on more classroom hours. These legislators seem to regard the educational system as essentially a system which transmits knowledge via the technology of the classroom to as large a number of students as possible, using as many faculty hours in the classroom as possible. An operations researcher who concentrated his time on planning universities of the future in terms of resources for teaching classes (buildings, faculty manpower, forecasts of student enrollment, etc.) might very well be solving precisely the wrong problem, *if* the problem of education is not the classroom but, rather, the way in which we can satisfy the universal need to know. To anyone who has reflected on the matter, the classroom is an extremely crude way of satisfying this need. It is wasteful of both faculty and student time and caters only to a certain style of learning, namely, one where ability to take in knowledge and retain it are the essential features. For example, one of the very best ways for many people to satisfy their need to know is to try to teach someone else. This way is completely blocked by the usual classroom-exposure type of education.

Finally, consider the system we call research. Here, the traditional way of looking at research is that certain people are qualified in terms of their learning and their mental qualifications (for example, intelligence) to conduct research and that society should fund the research with due regard to the "relevance" of the discipline to the good life and survival of the society. Opposed to this view of the research system is the notion that there is a universal need to discover—*not* that a researcher is a special kind of person, but that everyone is a special kind of researcher. If this is the case, then the basic question of the research system is no longer a question of which discipline should be supported but, rather, how we make research a more universally available activity for all individuals in our society. "Research" has become a bad word for the developing nations in the United Nations, because they see that under its slogan only the best qualified people in the world will be supported—namely, the people who live in the affluent nations. The developing nations may indeed be the wisest with respect to the system called research. They see that the research system, as it is now defined, serves the wrong client.

With this in hand, suppose we turn our idealism on libraries. Libraries are not separate systems. They are, indeed, a part of the health-education-research system. They are part of the health system in the sense that I just described, because they can reduce polarization in communities by helping the communities to become more aware

of themselves, of their history, and of their communities. The documentation of information that supports such awareness is essentially a "library" function. Libraries are a part of the educational system in the sense that the libraries of the future in a world of universal education will be totally unlike the libraries of today. The technology of such future libraries is to satisfy the universal need to know and not, as in the case of university libraries, to satisfy a specific clientele such as faculty or the qualified student. Finally, libraries are clearly a part of the research system, of the universal need to discover, because an exciting part of the activity of discovery consists of relating this activity to other discoveries and discoverers.

Hence, our concentration on making libraries "function better" may have the effect of solving precisely the wrong problem, *if* libraries are not in the document acquisition and retrieval business but, rather, in the universal health-education-research business. For example, it may be that libraries should be playing a far more active role in the community by becoming centers where people can go to express their ideas and learn about other people's ideas. In this case, the more or less passive document collection might play only a subsidiary role if the purpose of the library is to reduce polarization in a community rather than simply to store and transmit information.

There is another way, as there so often is, to pose the idealistic viewpoint. This is to turn our attention to the client or "user" of the library.

When information retrieval first began to appear as a systematic area of study, a number of us began to preach against the strategy of the information retrieval research. It seemed to us that information retrieval was concentrating on the wrong end of the spectrum; it was chiefly looking at document retrieval, abstracting, and indexing, and rarely if ever raising the question as to who the user was and what he should expect of the system. In other words, the strategy of the information retriever was very much like the strategy of the operations researcher discussed above, namely, he accepted the retrieval system as a given.

But our holier-than-thou attitude may have been a mistaken one. We have gradually begun to realize that the real user may not be classifiable in terms of his true need for information, except in the relatively unimportant cases of routine or bureaucratic retrievals. If the real user is unique in some very strong sense, then "classification" may only touch on the superficial aspects of his needs. Of course, the implications of this idea of user uniqueness are very obscure. If the library user has unique requirements not comparable to that of any other user, then any standard method of analysis and evaluation is bound to be

faulty because all such methods assume that people can be and ought to be classified. Even if the user is unique, it does not follow that libraries are ill designed; all that is implied is that we cannot evaluate the designs by classifying the users. For example, cost-benefit analysis, which is based on classification of people, is an inappropriate method.

Does the idealist challenge help? Which is more relevant: the practical, realistic inquiring system or the idealistic?

The first point to be made is that no one is obliged to respond to these questions. The second point is that the questions remain as central issues for all systems analysis, whether or not we make them conscious, for idealism-realism is an eternal dialectic, as I have tried to argue in *Challenge to Reason* [10]. The realist is practical, feasible, helpful, worldly, all of which are idealistic concepts, while the idealist is moral and concerned with *real* improvement, not the deceptively slick but costly "solution," attitudes which are very realistic.

REFERENCES

1. Churchman, C. W. *On the Design of Inquiring Systems.* New York: Basic Books, 1971.
2. Churchman, C. W. *The Systems Approach.* New York: Delacorte Press, 1968.
3. Bauer, Raymond A. *Social Indicators.* Cambridge, Mass.: M.I.T. Press, 1966.
4. Wagner, Harvey. *Principles of Operations Research.* Englewood Cliffs, N.J.: Prentice-Hall, Inc., 1969.
5. Forrester, J. W. *Industrial Dynamics.* Cambridge, Mass.: M.I.T. Press, 1961.
6. Forrester, J. W. *Urban Dynamics.* Cambridge, Mass.: M.I.T. Press, 1969.
7. Forrester, J. W. *World Dynamics.* Cambridge, Mass.: M.I.T. Press, 1971.
8. Echols, Michael E. "Budget Behavior and the Problem Formulation Process." Unpublished thesis, University of California, Berkeley, 1970.
9. Churchman, C. W., and Schainblatt, A. H. "The Researcher and the Manager: A Dialectic of Implementation." RAND Report P2984, 1964; also appears in *Management Science* 3 (February 1965): B69–B87.
10. Churchman, C. W. *Challenge to Reason.* New York: McGraw-Hill Book Co., 1968.

MEASURES OF LIBRARY EFFECTIVENESS[1]

PHILIP M. MORSE

ABSTRACT

Mathematical models of library operations are presented, allowing managers to estimate measures of effectiveness for a library. These models describe the amount of use made of resources by a user in a visit, the distribution of book circulation in a collection, the dependence of circulation on time, and the effect of multiple copies on user satisfaction. Predictions are made on the basis of the models of the consequences of breaking a central library into branch libraries. The effect, in terms of frustrated use, of removing the least-used books from a collection is discussed, as are strategies for for duplication. The emphasis is on facilitating getting results from models; for this purpose graphic techniques supplement the mathematical formulas.

INTRODUCTION

A few libraries consider their task to be that of collecting, storing, and preserving books. Most libraries consider it also their task to make these books available to their users. These libraries are service organizations, and must justify their budgets by the degree of service they render. To do this, the librarian will find it useful to quote measures of the degree to which his library is satisfying its clientele. Predictions of future measures are needed when he is weighing alternative plans for expansion or for changes in operating procedures. Monthly or yearly measures are then needed to use as a check on whether the results actually correspond to expectations with previously implemented plans or policies. As with any other operation, these measures—quantitative criteria—are a crucial part of the application of operations research to library management. Meaningful measures are particularly difficult to develop for public service

operations, where the profit motive is not paramount, but they are essential in these days of expanding demands, of increasing pressure on budgets, and of impending intrusion by the electronic computer.

A measure of effectiveness is a number designed to indicate the operational state of some part of the system. It is not usually obtained directly and simply from data. Most useful measures are obtained by processing the data by means of a mathematical model chosen to represent some part of the operation. The models are chosen to extend the range of the data and thus to simplify the task of data gathering; their use can allow one to display the results in a form most appropriate for policy decisions and for monitoring the consequences of these decisions. The model is in a form applicable to like operations under differing circumstances. Library models, for example, should apply to all libraries, although of course the values of the parameters used in the models will differ from library to library. Once the model is verified, the determination of the ap-

[1] This work was supported in part by contract no. DAHC04-70-C-0058, U.S. Army Research Office (Durham).

15

propriate values of the parameters for a given library is a much easier task than devising a new model or attempting to predict on the basis of data without a model.

This paper will present a few examples of the way models can extend the usefulness of data. In addition, it is a plea for more data gathering—not only blind collection of any sort of numbers, but an efficient assemblage of those data needed to use a tested model or the larger quantity required to test out a new model. The models presented in this paper are simple ones, dealing with only a few aspects of library operation. We need other models, dealing with other aspects, before the librarian can be armed with the variety of decision tools now available to managers of many other operations. For this goal to be reached, we need more data, both to extend present models and to test out proposed ones.

LIBRARY USE

Sometimes a model can be quite simple, and the data gathering can be quite straightforward. To find out how people use a library, we can distribute questionnaires asking what users do during a visit. A few hundred, distributed at random (say to every tenth visitor), would provide sufficient accuracy. They should be kept simple, asking only what is of interest at the moment, and asking only what actions are performed during the visit, not for opinions or estimates of past or future actions. If, for example, in a university library, the status (faculty or student) and department of the visitor were asked, together with the number of books (periodicals or reports) consulted in the library, the number taken out on loan, and the number of times

the visitor used the card catalog during that visit, these data would provide a useful picture of user habits. From the questionnaires, one could, for example, immediately calculate the average number of times per visit a chemist used the card catalog, or the number of books he borrowed or consulted in the library. The ratio of books consulted to books borrowed would enable one to estimate, for example, the relation between in-library use of a class of books and their circulation.

These direct measures are themselves useful in deciding what services and accommodations are needed by various users. For example, the facts that chemists using the Massachusetts Institute of Technology Science Library consult 4.4 books but only borrow 0.2 books per visit, on the average, and only consult the card catalog on one visit in three, whereas the mathematicians, on the average, consult only 2 books and borrow 0.4 books, but consult the catalog once per visit, tells us something of importance in the planning of a branch library for chemists or for mathematicians.

But if we add to these data the well-tested probability model of the modified geometric distribution [1, pp. 9–42; 2; 3; 4, pp. 56–133, 445–516] (sometimes called the Bradford or Zipf distribution), many details can be recovered, without having to gather additional data. In the first place, one can estimate the number of "visitors" who use the library as a study hall, without intending to use its books or other special facilities. From the questionnaires, we can determine the fraction of all visitors who perform one or more of any of the tasks (borrow or consult a book or use the catalog, in our example) included in the questionnaire, and can then calculate the average number of tasks, of any of the included ones, performed per visit *by those users who performed one or more tasks*. For the modified geometric distribution, this is equal to one plus the mean number of tasks K per visit performed by all *users,* including those who came intending to use the library, but, for various reasons, failed to perform any of the tasks under study. This more accurate measure, K, the mean number of tasks per visit *per potential user* (equal to the average number of tasks per user who performs one or more tasks, minus one), enables us to compute the rest of the details. Suppose your questionnaire shows that a fraction F_1 of visitors performed one or more of the tasks under study. Then F_1 times $(K+1)/K$ is the fraction of all vistors who are users (that is, who arrived intending to perform one or more of the tasks under study; some of these, of course, were prevented from

performing even one task, but they should be included in the list as "users," potential or actual). If $F_1(K+1)/K$ is appreciably less than 1, then the difference is the fraction of visitors who are nonusers. This inference from the model has been checked several times [5] at the M.I.T. Science Library. At one time, when nonusers rose to nearly half of the library visitors, it was found that Boston University students were using it as a comfortable, quiet study hall (ID cards were required for awhile thereafter, to discourage the non–Massachusetts Institute of Technology visitors). Once the fraction of nonusers is determined, the corresponding number can be subtracted from the questionnaires reporting no tasks, and the remainder is ready for further analysis.

For example, the fraction of users who perform m or more of the tasks under study is equal to G^m, where $G = (K/K+1)$. This can be quickly read off the chart of figure 1. The line, run-

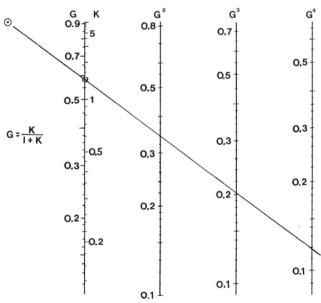

Fig. 1.—Relationship between mean number K of tasks per visit and powers of distribution parameter G.

ning through the circle in the upper left-hand corner of the graph and the point corresponding to K cuts the other lines at points corresponding to G^2, G^3, and G^4. The chart illustrates this for $K = 1.4$. We read off that $G = 0.58$, that the fraction of library users performing two or more tasks is $G^2 = 0.34$, and the fraction performing four or more tasks is $G^4 = 0.12$. To check the model, we can compare these predictions with the data from the questionnaires. The correspondence will of course only be approximate if the sample is small.

The model can be made more detailed in order to separate the different specific tasks covered in the questionnaire. Let us examine two tasks (for example, the number of books, bound periodicals, or reports borrowed and the number used in the library per visit), which we shall call tasks 1 and 2. From the questionnaires (after substracting the nonusers), we can calculate the mean numbers K_1 of task 1, and K_2 of task 2 performed per visit by users. Then the expected fraction of users who perform n_1 tasks and n_2 tasks per visit is:

$$P(n_1, n_2) = \frac{(n_1 + n_2)!}{n_1! \, n_2!}$$

$$\frac{K_1^{n_1} K_2^{n_2}}{(1 + K_1 + K_2)^{n_1 + n_2 + 1}}. \quad (1)$$

(Those not interested in equations can simply skip them and concentrate on the tables and figures, which tell the same story.) This reduces to our earlier formula, for if $K = K_1 + K_2$ is the total number of tasks performed, then the expected fraction of users who perform n tasks, no matter what the proportion between 1 and 2, is the sum of $P(n_1, n - n_1)$ over n_1 from 0 to n, which equals:

$$P(n) = (1 - G)G^n;$$

$$G = K/(1 + K). \quad (2)$$

Furthermore, the probability of a user performing n_1 tasks, irrespective of how many tasks 2 he performed during the visit, is the sum of $P(n_1, n_2)$ over all values of n_2, which is:

$$P(n_1) = (1 - G_1)(G_1)^{n_1};$$

$$G_1 = K_1/(1 + K_1). \quad (3)$$

But more interesting than these internal checks of the model are the additional predictions one can make. For example, the mean number of tasks 1 done per visit by those who perform n_2 tasks 2 during the same visit is:

$$(n_2 + 1) \frac{K_1}{K_2 + 1}. \quad (4)$$

The dependence on n_2 of the number of tasks 1 performed is due in part to the fact that the more tasks are done by a visitor the longer (on the average) is his stay and the greater is his chance to do other tasks. The mean number of tasks 1 done by a visitor who does at least one task 2 during his visit is:

$$(K_2 + 2) \frac{K_1}{K_2 + 1}. \quad (5)$$

As an example, we mention some of the predictions which can be made from a set of sample questionnaires asking chemists and mathematicians how many books (periodicals or reports) they borrowed or consulted and how many times they used the catalog per visit. After eliminating the nonusers, we calculate the three mean task numbers K, as indicated previously, and can apply equations (3)–(5). Typ-

TABLE 1

TYPICAL RESULTS FOR K, THE MEAN NUMBER OF TASKS PER VISIT PER POTENTIAL USER

USER CLASS	K_n (Av. No. Tasks per Visit)			FRACTION VISITS CONSULTING MORE THAN 1 BOOK	AV. BOOKS BORROWED BY CONSULTANTS OF 1 OR MORE BOOKS	FRACTION VISITS NOT USING CATALOG	AV. BOOKS BORROWED BY THOSE USING CATALOG
	Books Borrowed	Books Consulted	Catalog Used				
Chemist	0.2	4.4	0.3	0.67	0.23	0.77	0.35
Mathematician	0.4	2.0	1.0	0.44	0.53	0.50	0.60

ical results for the K's, again from the M.I.T. Science Library, [5] are shown in table 1, in the first three columns. These K's are all the calculations one needs to make from the data. Equations (3) and (5) enable one to predict the fractions given in the last four columns. One also can see that, on the average, chemists use twenty-two times as many books in the library as they borrow, whereas mathematicians use only 2.5 times as many books in the library as they borrow.

DEPARTMENT LIBRARIES

A rather more interesting deduction from this same model comes when we gather data on the different classes of books used by different classes of users of the same library. Suppose chemists (class 1) use (borrow or consult) physics books (periodicals or reports) on the average, K_{12} times per visit; whereas physicists (class 2) use chemistry books an average of K_{21} times per visit. These visits are to a single library, containing both physics and chemistry books. On the other hand, if these collections were in separate libraries, whenever a chemist wished to use 1 or more physics books, he would have to go to the physics library, thus adding $G_{12} = K_{12}/(1 + K_{12})$ trips, since this is the fraction of his trips to

the unified library during which he used 1 or more physics books.[2] A similar argument holds for the physicist; to use the same books, for a fraction $G_{21} = K_{21}/(1 + K_{21})$ of his trips to the physics library, he will have to make an extra trip to the chemistry library. The fractional increase in trips made by both classes of user is:

$$\frac{X_1 + X_2}{V_1 + V_2}; X_1 = V_1 G_{12}, X_2 = V_2 G_{21},$$

(6)

where V_1 and V_2 are the number of visits paid to the combined library by chemists or physicists, respectively, during the sampled period. The calculation can be made graphically by the use of figure 2. The diagonal line illustrates its use for $V_2/V_1 = 0.5$ (chemists' visits are twice those of physicists) and for $K_{12} = 0.5$ and $K_{21} = 1.4$. The line drawn from the point $K_{12} = 0.5$, $(V_2/V_1) = 0.5$ to the point, $K_{21} = 1.4$, $(V_2/V_1) = 0.5$ crosses the heavy vertical line at 0.42. In this case, therefore, 42 percent more trips are forced on the chemists and physicists by separating the collections. Of course this fraction could be reduced by buying some phys-

[2] This approximation does not consider the case in which a chemist decides to use a physics book, but *no* chemistry book. For such a case, no extra trip would occur.

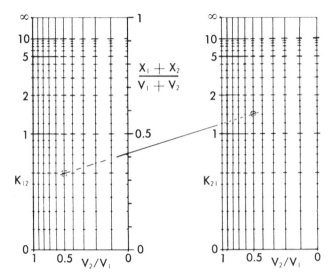

$$\frac{X_1 + X_2}{V_1 + V_2}$$

Fig. 2.—Graphic determination of fractional increase in trips required by a divided library over that for a unified library. See text for details.

ics books to put in the chemistry library and vice versa. But *how much* this would help the situation, and *how much* extra it would cost, can be determined only by use of a book circulation model, which we turn to next.

BOOK USE

Since we are interested in large numbers of books, our attitude can be rather like that of an insurance company, which loses in a few cases but wins on the average. Our models need not predict the use of a particular book as long as they can predict the average behavior of all books of a class. And even these average predictions need not be exceptionally precise; it is much better to us a model which requires few data and predicts within a possible error of 25 percent, than to use one which predicts with great accuracy but requires man-years of effort to acquire the data for its implementation.

Library books are used in the library or (in some cases) are with-

drawn on loan. Data on the circulation of those books which can be withdrawn may usually be obtained from the book cards. Sufficient accuracy can be achieved by examining the cards from several hundred books of a given class (chemistry or recent history books or all the books on English history, for example). The cards examined should be taken from a random sample of the class; every tenth book on the shelf may be used, for example, or every thirtieth, as long as the sample covers all the shelves occupied by the class and as long as the resulting sample is several hundred. Samples of cards of books in circulation should also be taken, in the same proportions. One need not examine all classes in the same month; the survey can be spread over several years if manpower is in short supply. The resulting measures do not change much, from year to year, unless the collection is radically modified, or its location is drastically changed, or the library users change markedly in their interests. They may be expected to differ from book class to book class, and from library to library.

From each card, one records the number of circulations in the past year and the number in the previous year (books on the shelf less than two years are recorded in a separate list). These pairs of numbers are the data from which one obtains the circulation measures for books of the class under study.

In the first place, the circulation figures for the last year give us the distribution in circulation for the class. This turns out to be, approximately, a modified geometric distribution of the sort discussed earlier in this paper. From the data one can calculate the fraction $C(t)$ of books in the sample which circulated one or more times during the past year (which we shall call the *active books* in the collection) and also the mean circulation of the active fraction:

tend these measures to estimate details of the circulation behavior of books of the class under study, during the past year. For example, the fraction of the class which circulated n or more times in that year is approximately:

$$F_n(t) = C(t) [G_c(t)]^{n-1}$$

$$(n > 0), \quad (9)$$

where $G_c(t) = K_c(t)/[K_c(t) + 1] = 1 - [C(t)/\overline{R}(t)]$, a set of quantities which can be obtained from the chart of figure 1. They indicate how many duplicate copies should be obtained, as explained below.

As we shall see later, the mean circulation of a given collection of books decreases with time. However, the mean circulation of all the books of a given class in many libraries remains fairly constant, because the older books are constantly being replenished by newer and more popular books. Therefore, in many cases, we can consider the measures $\overline{R}$ and C for all the books of a

$$\overline{R}_a(t) = \frac{\text{total circulation of sample during past year}}{\text{no. in sample circulating one or more times in past year}}$$

$$= \frac{\overline{R}(t)}{C(t)} = K_c(t) + 1. \quad (7)$$

The fraction $P_0(t)$ of books of the sampled class which did not circulate at all in the past year (the inactive fraction), and also the past year's mean circulation $R(t)$ *of all books* of the sampled class, may then be computed from these two numbers:

$$P_0(t) = 1 - C(t),$$

$$\overline{R}(t) = C(t) \cdot \overline{R}_a(t),$$

$$(8)$$

which are two of the four measures of circulation for books of the class. Finally, the modified geometric model [1, pp. 123–51; 6, 7] enables us to ex-

class to be more or less independent of time; the quantity which is changing is the total number of books in the class.

The $\overline{R}$ and C for new books can be obtained from the sample data for books that have been on the shelf less than two years. They are measures of the effectiveness of the purchasing policies.

DUPLICATE REQUIREMENTS FOR DIVIDED LIBRARIES

Thus the fraction of the active books in a class (that is, those that circulate during the year) which circulate n times during the year is $(F_n/C) = [1 - C/\overline{R})]^{n-1}$, where we have left off the dependence on time. The mean circulation of this fraction which circulate n times is $[n + (\overline{R}/C) - 1]F_n$. This formula can be inverted to express the fraction of the total circulation E_n carried by those books that circulate n times, in terms of (F_n/C) and $C/\overline{R}$):

$$E_n = \left(\frac{C}{\overline{R}}\right)\left\{\frac{\ln(F_n/C)}{\ln[1 - (C/\overline{R})]} + 1\right\}$$
$$\left(\frac{F_n}{C}\right), \quad (10)$$

where (F_n/C) is the fraction of active books of the class that circulate n and $(\overline{R}/C)$ is the mean circulation of all the active books in the class. This fraction E_n of total circulation carried turns out to be approximately independent of $(\overline{R}/C)$ when this quantity is between 1.5 and 4 and when (F_n/C) is less than 0.4. The approximate values of E_n for values of (F_n/C) are shown in table 2.

TABLE 2

FRACTION E_n OF TOTAL CIRCULATION CARRIED BY THE FRACTION (F_n/C) OF THE ACTIVE BOOKS WHICH CIRCULATE THE GREATEST NUMBER OF TIMES

(F_n/C)	0.5	0.10	0.20	0.30	0.40
E_n	0.13	0.22	0.33	0.41	0.46

We see that the most active twentieth of the active books of a class generate one-eighth of the circulation and that the most active fifth generate a third of the total circulation. These results can now be applied to the problem of the divided library, which we discussed earlier. We could attempt to reduce the number of extra trips made by chemists to the physics library, and

vice versa, by adding duplicates of the most active physics books to the chemistry library and active chemistry books to the physics library. But we see that adding the most active fifth of the physics books to the chemistry library will serve only a third of the chemists' needs for physics books. Even this fraction of the active physics books requires a large additional outlay to provide so many duplicate books. It is possible that careful choice by the chemists of those books particularly useful to them, rather than a general provision of highly active books, would reduce the number required to satisfy up to one-third of the chemists' needs. But the very statistical nature of book use would make it quite impossible to reduce the chemists' visits to the physics library by as much as a half, without the purchase of an unacceptably high number of duplicates of physics books. The conclusion seems to be that whenever users of one class use as many as 1 book per visit of another class, a separation of the two classes of books into two libraries is bound to lead to difficulties.

DEPENDENCE OF CIRCULATION ON TIME

The Markov model [1, pp. 83–110] indicates that the two measures, C and $\overline{R}$, for a specific collection of books (without new ones being added), change from year to year in accordance with a second pair of measures, α and β. The mean circulation of the collection in year t is approximately related to its mean circulation a year previously, in year $t - 1$, by the simple formula:

$$\overline{R}(t) = \alpha + \beta\,\overline{R}(t - 1). \quad (11)$$

Circulation parameter β measures how rapidly the "popularity" of a book of the class diminishes from year to year. If β is not much smaller than unity, the mean circulation in year t will not be much less than it was in the previous year; but if β is considerably smaller than one, mean circulation will drop considerably in the first few years the book is on the shelf. Parameter α measures the asymptotic circulation, the value which the mean circulation of older books of the class eventually reaches. Parameter β must be less than unity and is usually between 0.2 and 0.8; parameter α could be larger than unity, but is usually between 0.3 and 0.7. Data taken so far indicate that β stays roughly constant for ten or twenty years, whereas α drops slowly to about 2/3 its initial value after ten or twelve years of a book's life in the library.

To calculate α and β for books of the class under study, we take the list of circulations for two successive years, recorded for the sample, and divide the list according to the circulation in the earliest year. We calculate the mean circulation in the past year, $R_m(t)$, for all those books in the sample that had circulated m times in the previous year. For example, if 20 books in the sample each had circulated exactly twice during the year before last, and if the total circulation of these 20 during *last* year had been 32, the $R_2(t)$ for this sample would be 1.6; and if the 80 books which did not circulate in the year before last (the inactive books of that year) had a total circulation of 32 last year, the $R_0(t)$ would be 0.4. Note that a book which is inactive one year can be active next year; this is the case in actuality, and is a basic part of the Markov model.

We compute $R_0(t)$, $R_1(t)$, $R_2(t)$, $R_3(t)$, $R_4(t)$, from the data for the sample (if there are no books in the sample which circulated m times during the year before last (for $m = 0, 1, 2, 3, 4$), then our sample is not large enough). One way to calculate α and β for the sampled class is then to use the following equations:

$$\alpha = R_0(t); \beta = \frac{1}{10}[R_1(t) + R_2(t)$$

$$+ R_3(t) + R_4(t) - 4R_0(t)]. \quad (12)$$

Purists may prefer to solve for α and β by least squares; those preferring graphical methods can plot $R_m(t)$ against m, draw a straight line fitting the points as well as possble, and read α from the intercept for $m = 0$ and β from the slope of the line. In any case, the parameters thus determined, for the class of books sampled, change little from year to year (as mentioned). As long as the collection is not changed radically in size or in location, a pair of values for a given class need not be reevaluated more than once in four or five years. If a few new books are added each year to the collection, these parameters may hardly change at all in ten years.

Note that the models themselves, the formulas, and/or the graphical aids to calculation shown in the figures, are the same for all libraries (within the degree of approximation inherent in any statistical model), but the individual values of the constants differ from library to library and from class to class. In fact, the α and β for a given class of books (those on chemistry, for example) may be quite different in different libraries, particularly when the clientele differ. Thus the measures C, $\overline{R}$, and α and β must be determined for each case. But the data needed to determine these measures for a checked-out model are very much less than the data needed to develop a new model.

It would be useful to obtain measures $C(t)$, $R(t)$, α, and β as well for the in-library use of the same class of books, but present procedures in many libraries do not keep records of in-library use. Until the computer can be used for record keeping, we must be satisfied to estimate in-library use from circulation data, using the questionnaires mentioned earlier to obtain ratios of in-library to loan use for various classes of books.

PREDICTION OF CIRCULATION MEASURES

Once measures α and β for the change in circulation with age have been determined for a given class of books in a given library, they can be used to predict a large number of use-properties of books of the class. The Markov model [1, pp. 83–110] enables us to predict the measures $C(t+1)$ and $\overline{R}(t+1)$ for the same collection during its next year, $t+1$, in terms of the measures $C(t)$, $\overline{R}(t)$ for the past year and the parameters α and β, which remain fairly constant for a given collection for several years (as long as the collection is not radically changed in composition or in location). The equations for $\overline{R}(t+1)$, $\overline{R}(t+2)$, $\overline{R}(t+n)$, the expected mean circulation for the collection in successive years after the present, are:

$$\overline{R}(t+1) = \alpha + \beta\,\overline{R}(t),$$

$$\overline{R}(t+2) = \alpha + \beta\,\overline{R}(t+1) \qquad (13)$$
$$= \alpha(1+\beta) + \beta^2\,\overline{R}(t)$$

$$\overline{R}(t+n) = \alpha(1+\beta) + \beta^2 \ldots$$
$$+ \beta^{n-1} + \beta^n \overline{R}(t).$$

Note that, for any individual book of the class, such predictions of $\overline{R}(t+n)$, in terms of the circulation $\overline{R}(t)$ of the individual book during the past year, may differ considerably from the actual circulation of the book as it occurs in successively later years. But the actual circulations will exceed the predictions about as often as they fall below them, and the *average* circulation behavior of a whole collection of several hundred books of a class will correspond fairly closely with the predictions of equations (13) [1, pp. 161–64; 8; 9]. Since the librarian usually is dealing with large numbers of books, his best bet is to err high as often as low, in other words, to use the average predictions of equations (13).

To use the circulation model of equations (8) and (9) for future years we must also predict $C(t+n)$, the fraction of active books in the collection n year later. From $C(t+n)$ and $R(t+n)$ for the nth later year, we can then work out further details as required. The model requires that $1 - C(t+1) = P_0(t+1)$, the inactive fraction of the collection during next year, is given by the formula:

$$P_0(t+1) = e^{-\alpha}\,[1 - H(t)];$$
$$H(t) = \frac{C(t)}{1 + J(t)}; \qquad (14)$$

$$J(t) = \frac{C(t)/\overline{R}(t)}{e^\beta - 1}.{}^3$$

This formula can be expressed graphically by the set of charts shown in

---

[3] This follows if we assume that the probability of n circulations next year for a book that circulates m times this year is given by a Poisson distribution around the mean $\alpha + \beta m$.

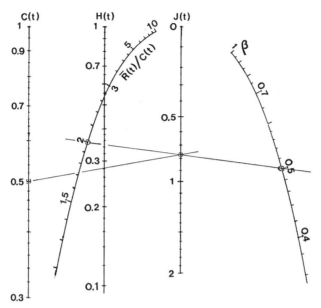

Fig. 3.—Graphic determination of expected fraction of books of a given collection, which will be active next year, in terms of present active fraction $C(t)$, present mean circulation $R(t)$, and Markov parameters α and β for the same books. This figure is to be used together with figure 4.

figures 3 and 4. Using figure 3, we first run a straightedge between the point for $\overline{R}(t)/C(t)$ the mean circulation in the past year of the active books of that year) and the point for

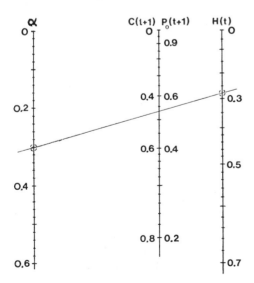

Fig. 4.—Continuation of figure 3; see text for details.

the predetermined β. This crosses the center line at the point corresponding to $J(t)$. A straightedge run from this point to the point for the measured value of $C(t)$ (the active fraction in the past year) crosses the middle vertical line at the point corresponding to the value of $H(t)$. Turning to figure 4, we place a straightedge between the point for the value of $H(t)$ just determined from figure 3, to the point for the predetermined α. Where this crosses the middle line, we can read off the predicted value of $C(t+1)$ (the active fraction) or of $P_0(t+1) = 1 - C(t+1)$ (the inactive fraction) for the coming year. Note that it is not necessarily the same books which are inactive in successive years; we are simply calculating the fraction of the collection that do not circulate; not which books do not.

In the figures, the lines are drawn to correspond to a collection for which

$\overline{R}(t) = 1$, $C(t) = 0.5$ during the past year, $\alpha = 0.3$, and $\beta = 0.5$. From equation (12) we find that $R(t + 1) = 0.8$ and from figure 3 we see that $J(t) = 0.67$ and $H(t) = 0.28$, and from figure 4 we see that $C(t + 1) = 0.47$. Thus in the coming year, the mean circulation and the fraction of the collection which circulates are expected to be somewhat smaller than they were for the past year. To find the predictions for two years from now, we recompute, using the new values of $\overline{R}$ and C, but the same values of α and β. Note that the smaller the value of β the larger is $J(t)$ and thus the smaller is $H(t)$ and, from figure 4, the smaller is $C(t + 1)$, the predicted fraction of the collection which will be active next year. This is understandable, for if β is small, the mean circulation drops more rapidly with time, and this, in turn, implies that the active fraction of the collection will also drop rapidly.

With both $C(t + 1)$ and $\overline{R}(t + 1)$ predicted, we are able to compute other circulation details. For example, since $G_c(t + 1) = 1 - [C(t+1)/\overline{R}(t + 1]$ is 0.41, whereas $G_c(t) = 0.5$, the fraction of the collection that will circulate two or more times next year is $C(t + 1) [G_c(t + 1)]^2$ from equation (9) and, from figure 1 for the case just discussed, is $0.47 \times (0.41)^2 = 0.08$. Only 1 book in 12 of the same collection is expected to circulate more than once next year, whereas 1 book in 8 of the same collection circulated more than once during the past year.

EFFECTS OF RETIRING
INACTIVE BOOKS

A somewhat more interesting problem is to see what would happen if the half of this collection which was inactive last year were removed to some less-accessible region. We find that the predicted mean circulation next year of the active half, which remains in place, would be 1.3, since $C(t) = 1$ (all this half circulated last year) and $\overline{R}(t) = 2$ (the mean circulation of this half is twice that of the whole) and $\alpha + 2\beta = 1.3$. This assumes that α and β of the remaining active half are the same as those for the previous whole.

The actual mean circulation may be somewhat more than this, but not much. The α and β for the active fraction of a collection seem to be about the same as for the inactive fraction. If the α and β for the inactive half, relegated to a less-accessible region, were not to change, we would expect the mean circulation of this half to be 0.3 circulations per year per volume (as pointed out before, the Markov model includes the fact that some volumes which do not circulate during one year may circulate the next). The mean circulation of both halves would then be $(1/2)(1.3 + 0.3) = 0.8$, which checks the figure predicted for the collection if it were all to remain in its original location. But data have shown that relegating a collection to basement stacks reduces the α for that collection by a factor of about 2/3. Thus, we can expect that the mean circulation of the relegated half would be more nearly 0.2 than 0.3 next year.

If the total collection were to consist of 2,000 volumes, 2,000 circulations would have occurred during the past year $[\overline{R}(t) = 1]$ and 1,600 would have occurred the next year if it were all left in its original location. If half were taken to a less-accessible spot, the remaining 1,000 volumes would produce 1,300 circulations and the 1,000 in the nether regions would produce only 200. Thus, of the 1,600 circulations that would have occurred from the undisturbed collection next year, about 82 percent of the borrowers will not be inconvenienced by the separation, about 12 percent will be inconvenienced but will get their book from the basement anyway, and about 6 percent will not bother to go to the extra trouble (or will not be able to find the book in its new location).

WHEN TO BUY A DUPLICATE COPY

Finally, we can combine the Markov model with the queuing model for circulation interference [1, pp. 54–82]. This model indicates that, if a single-copy book circulates R times in a given year, if there had been 2 copies of the book on the shelves, the total yearly circulation of the 2 volumes would be roughly $R + R^2/\mu$), as long as (R/μ) is 1/2 or less. In this formula, $(1/\mu)$ is the mean fraction of a year the book is off the shelf during a single loan period (for a two-week book, with single renewals allowed, μ is approximately 20). Thus (R/μ) is the fraction of a year the single book is off the shelf during its R circulations, and therefore is the fraction of time prospective borrowers would not find it if there were no duplicate copy available. The duplicate copy would not cure all this circulation interference, for part of the time both copies will be out on loan. Nevertheless, the model predicts that, on the average, (R^2/μ) of these frustrated borrowers will be served by the presence of the duplicate.

One sees that if (R/μ) is very small, it is not worth adding a duplicate, so there must be a minimal value of R below which it is not "worthwhile" to buy a duplicate, above which it is. One

also sees that one can only be sure of the value of R for a book after the first year has passed (or, at best, after six months on the shelf). But a duplicate can improve service only *after* it gets on the shelf, and it takes time to order and to process a duplicate. Suppose we find, after six months, that a particular book is popular enough to warrant buying a duplicate. It will take nearly six months to get the duplicate on the shelf, so it can take its part in raising circulation only *after* the first year. To decide whether the duplicate is "worth" buying we must be able to predict the circulation of the present single volume next year and for subsequent years. And for this we use the Markov model, together with the queuing model.

The combined models state that, if a book turns out to circulate $R(1)$ times during its first year, its total circulation, without a duplicate, during its next ten years in the library, is expected to be, approximately,

$$R_{10} = \frac{10\alpha + \beta R(1)}{1 - \beta} - \frac{\alpha\beta}{(1 - \beta)^2}, \quad (15)$$

where α and β are the parameters for the class of books to which the volume belongs. Since this is an individual book, this formula may differ considerably from the actual ten-year record for the book, but as a prediction for the average ten-year circulation for a number of books of the same class, it is a pretty good approximation.

Using the formula $[R^2(t)/\mu]$ for the additional circulation generated by a duplicate, for each year the duplicate is on the shelf we can compute the increase in circulation R_d, over and above R_{10}, produced by having the duplicate present from the second through the eleventh year of the original copy's shelf life. The result is, roughly,

$$R_d = \frac{1}{\mu}\left\{\left(\frac{\alpha}{1-\beta}\right)^2\left(10 - \frac{1+\beta}{1-\beta}\right) + \left[\frac{\alpha}{1-\beta} + \beta R(1)\right]^2\left(\frac{1}{1-\beta^2}\right)\right\}.$$

(16)

This, in general, is less than R_{10}, but the policy question is how big should it be before we decide to buy a duplicate in time to have it on the shelf by the beginning of the second year of the original?

One way of deciding is to compare R_d with the mean circulation of all books in the library. If the R_d for a given book, with first-year circulation $R(1)$, is greater than ten times this mean circulation, then it will be contributing, during the ten years, as much to the library's service to its users as the average book on the shelves does. Another way is to compare it with the mean circulation of all first-year books. If $(R_d/10)$ is greater than this mean first-year circulation, the contribution of the duplicate per year is greater than that of the average new book which is bought, and, in terms of service to the library users, it deserves to be bought instead of another new book.

The calculation of R_d can be facilitated by using the graph of figure 5. One runs a straightedge between the point corresponding to $[\alpha/(1-\beta)]$ on the vertical line corresponding to β, with the point corresponding to the value of $[\alpha/(1-\beta)] + \beta R(1)$ on the other β line. Where the straightedge cuts the center line, one reads off the value of μR_d, divides by μ, and obtains the value of R_d to be used in deciding whether to buy a duplicate or not.

In the example shown by the upper

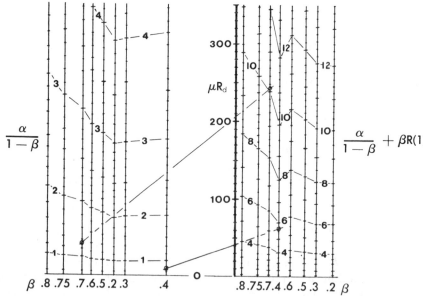

FIG. 5.—Determination of additional circulation generated by a duplicate copy, during the second to eleventh year of shelf life of the first copy, in terms of first-year circulation $R(1)$ of first copy, of the Markov parameters α and β for books of this class and of the mean loan period $(1/\mu)$.

diagonal line, we have chosen the case of a book of a class which has $\alpha = 0.4$, $\beta = 0.7$, and which circulated 12.5 times during its first year. Then $[\alpha/(1-\beta)] = 1.33$, $[\alpha/(1-\beta)] + \beta R(1) = 10.08$, and $\mu R_d = 205$. If $\mu = 20$, then $R_d = 10.25$, and the duplicate adds an average of one circulation per year for ten years. In a library which has an average of one circulation per volume per year for its whole collection, this value of R_d could be large enough to warrant buying the duplicate. But if $\beta = 0.4$ instead of 0.7, and α, μ, and $R(1)$ remain the same, then $[\alpha/(1-\beta)] = 0.67$, $\beta R(1) + [\alpha/(1-\beta)] = 5.67$, and the lower diagonal line indicates that $\mu R_d = 40$, and, if $\mu = 20$, $R_d = 2$. The circulation of this book falls off so rapidly (β is smaller) that by the end of two or three years its circulation, as a single copy, is only one or two per year; a duplicate would add very little extra circulation. Thus, the value of adding a duplicate depends strongly on the parameter β, which measures the speed with which circulation of the class decreases with time. Any simple rule which adds a duplicate whenever the first-year circulation of *any* books exceeds a certain value, would either result in many duplicates that are not needed or else in too few duplicates for books with long-lasting popularity (β near unity).

The analysis also points up the importance of recognizing a high-circulation book as early as possible in its shelf life, since the need for a duplicate is greatest at the beginning. One procedure to aid in early warning is to use a special book card in all new books, one which has only a small number of entry lines, six or eight, for example. When this card is filled, and a standard card is to be substituted to replace it, the circulation department can examine the filled card to see how long the book has been in the library. If all the circulations recorded on this card are within a year, there is a presumption that the book needs a duplicate, and such cards can be sent to the purchasing department for final decision, where, it is hoped, the predictions inherent in figure 5 will be used.

It should be pointed out again that the use of the Markov model to predict future circulation of individual books is only borne out in the mean. As with any actuarial statement, the correspondence with individual cases varies considerably—some books will exceed the prediction, others will fail to meet it. Nevertheless, a policy based on the prediction will be the best one can devise, on the average, considering the great degree of variability present; unless additional knowledge is available about the future use of a particular book (its use in a class, for example), the predictions of the model form the best possible basis for decisions. The model, of course, can estimate the chances that a book's circulation will overshoot or undershoot the prediction by a given amount, if this would be useful in reaching a decision.

CONCLUSIONS

We have given a few examples of the way a few simple models can translate raw data into measures which can aid in reaching operational policy decisions in regard to library service. It is to be hoped that more sampling methods can be devised for gathering other sorts of data, on other aspects of library operation, which can then use other tested models to develop measures of effectiveness. As the electronic computer comes to be integrated more economically into library operations, this data gathering and the subsequent generation of such measures will become easier. But work must precede these future aids. We must learn by experience which measures are most useful in monitoring library effectiveness, so we can ensure that the computers, when they arrive, will be designed to tell us what we need to know.

REFERENCES

1. Morse, Philip M. *Library Effectiveness: A Systems Approach.* Cambridge, Mass.: M.I.T. Press, 1968.
2. Leimkuhler, Ferdinand F. "The Bradford Distribution." *Journal of Documentation* 23 (1967): 197–207.
3. Goffman, W., and Morris, T. G. "Bradford's Law and Library Acquisitions." *Nature* 226 (1970): 922–23.
4. Zipf, George K. *Human Behavior and the Principle of Least Effort.* Cambridge, Mass.: Addison-Wesley Publishing Co., 1949.
5. Bush, G. C.; Galliher, H. P.; and Morse, P. M. "Attendance and Use of the Science Library at M.I.T." *American Documentation* 7 (1956): 87–100.
6. Jain, A. K., and Leimkuhler, F. F. "A Statistical Model of Book Use." *Journal of the American Statistical Association* 64 (1969): 1211–24.
7. Fussler, H. H., and Simon, J. L. *Patterns in the Use of Books in Large Research Libraries.* Chicago: University of Chicago Library, 1961.
8. Trueswell, Richard W. "Two Characteristics of Circulation." *College and Research Libraries* 25 (1964): 285–91.
9. Trueswell, Richard W. "A Quantitative Measure of User Circulation Requirements and Its Possible Effect on Stack Thinning and Multiple Copy Determination." *American Documentation* 16 (January 1965): 20–25.

GRAPH MODELS FOR LIBRARY INFORMATION NETWORKS

ROBERT R. KORFHAGE, U. NARAYAN BHAT, AND RICHARD E. NANCE

ABSTRACT

The design and study of library information networks are enhanced by the use of the concepts which have been developed by graph theorists. In this paper we expand upon this theme, proposing a general network structure which we believe to be a good model for a wide variety of library and other information networks. The basic concepts from graph theory are illustrated with the aid of a hypothetical Public Library Access Network (PLAN).

THE DESIGN OF PLAN

The word "graph" is used in many different ways, by both mathematicians and nonmathematicians. However, to the graph theorist this word has one precise meaning. It does not refer to bar charts, or to the curves which trace the values of mathematical functions. Rather, a graph (shown in fig. 1) is a structure which is intuitively associated with figures constructed of lines and points [1]. In particular, we shall be concerned with *directed graphs* or *digraphs* [2], whose lines have an orientation *from* one point *into* another (fig. 2). Precisely, a digraph consists of a finite set of *nodes* $n_1, n_2, \ldots, n_k$, and a finite set of *arcs* $a_1, a_2, \ldots, a_h$, such that to each arc is associated an ordered pair of nodes. If to arc a_i is associated the node pair (n_s, n_t), we then say that a_i is an arc *from* n_s *into* n_t and indicate this by an arrow on the picture of the digraph (see fig. 2).

To illustrate the use of digraphs in the study of information networks, let us consider a hypothetical network called PLAN (Public Library Access Network). The purpose of PLAN is to provide the library users of the forty-eight adjacent states and the District of Columbia with a system which will enable them to access any library anywhere within the territory covered. For purposes of exposition, we shall assume that there are only forty-nine libraries in the network and shall discuss the possible distribution and interconnection of these libraries. In addition to the provision of service, we might also want to impose other constraints on the system, such as easy access, rapid response, low cost, and the control of information flow within the network.

Let us consider, first, the distribution of the forty-nine libraries. This distribution can be determined by a number of different criteria. We might choose, for example, to distribute the libraries equally in terms of the area served. This would provide one library for each 61,700 square miles. While such a distribution might have some advantages in terms of cost or other factors, it intuitively does not appear to serve the population equally.

If we think in terms of the state library systems, one natural distribution of the libraries would be to place one in each state capital and one in Washington. Again, such a distribution would have both advantages and dis-

31

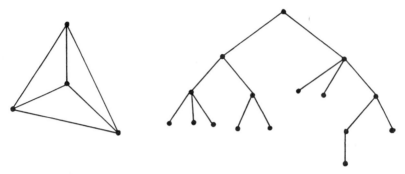

FIG. 1.—Two examples of graphs

advantages. Since libraries are intended to serve people, a better plan might be to place a library in each of the forty-nine largest cities. Alternatively, one might distribute the libraries, one per 4,080,000 people. We might suggest many other possible arrangements of the libraries, and, even within the arrangements which we have outlined, there is room for variation, such as, where within a city, state, or area one should place the library for maximum benefit. Each suggested placement of the libraries will have certain advantages and disadvantages in terms of cost, service, and the other constraints imposed on the network. Thus, the decision between the proposed placements is not a simple one.

If our network is to be usable by the public, then there must be more than the forty-nine libraries specified by us. As we include additional libraries, two major problems loom. First, can we design the network in stages, adding a second set of libraries to the original forty-nine library network, then another set, and so forth? Or do we need to redesign the whole network every time we enlarge it? Second, as more libraries are included in the network, among them will probably be some which are more specialized and differentiated. We will find, not only the public library, but also the university library, specialized libraries relating to particular industries or other groups of users, and probably even computer data banks. It seems reasonable to expect that these differentiated libraries will play quite different roles in the total network.

But let us return to our main network, with forty-nine libraries. At this point we have merely a set of libraries —the nodes in our digraph. To continue the construction of our model, we must add the arcs of the graph. These arcs correspond to the information-transfer paths of the network. Along some of the paths flow messages requesting information. Other paths carry documents in response to infor-

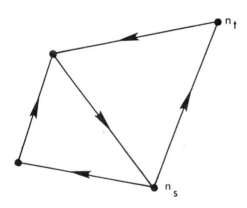

FIG. 2.—An example of a digraph

mation requests. Still others may carry both messages and documents. In any case, a great many possible paths exist for our network. While in actuality these paths may be chosen in a rather complex pattern, we find it convenient to discuss four "pure" types of networks.

In a *cyclic* network there is precisely one arc leading into each node and one arc leading from each node. These arcs are so chosen that the entire configuration forms one cycle or loop, with no repeated arcs or nodes (fig. 3).

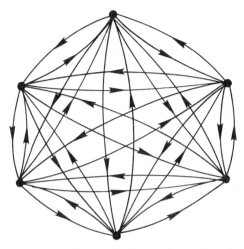

Fig. 4.—The decentralized network on six nodes

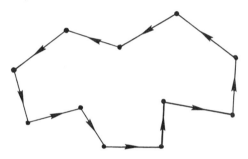

Fig. 3.—A cyclic network on eleven nodes

Such a network is relatively inexpensive to install,[1] provided that the arcs join nodes which are close together. However, since only one path exists from one node to any other, response time might be rather lengthy. The trade-off between installation cost and response time thus emerges.

A *decentralized* network provides immediate access from each node to every other one by an arc joining each pair of nodes (fig. 4). This type of network has the maximum number of arcs, and hence installation is quite

[1] By "installation" we mean the process of bringing the connecting arc structure into existence. In some cases existing information transfer channels (the mail, telephone lines, etc.) can be used; in other situations equipment must be set up.

costly. The PLAN network, for example, would have 2,352 lines, some stretching across the continent.

One characteristic shared by both the cyclic and the decentralized networks is the absence of a natural head, or main library. This may be either an advantage or a disadvantage. If one deems it a disadvantage, then a *hierarchical* network should be considered (fig. 5). This type of network provides, as does the cyclic network, a single path from any one node to any other; hence, relatively long response time might be expected. But since it is organized as a branching tree, the hierarchical network provides for relatively simple monitoring and control of the information flow.

Both the cyclic and the hierarchical networks suffer from another defect. Since there is only a single path from any one node to any other, the breaking of a single arc (information-transfer channel) in the network is enough to disrupt communications. At least one node will not be able to access one or more other nodes. The decentralized network is *reliable* in the sense that

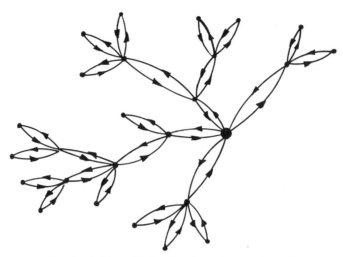

FIG. 5.—A hierarchical network on twenty-six nodes

breaking one arc will not disrupt information transfer: there are always other paths to follow. However, as we mentioned earlier, this type of network involves so many arcs that it is quite expensive. Suppose that we impose the following reliability criterion on the network: from any node to any other node there must be at least two information-transfer paths which have no arcs or nodes in common (other than the end nodes). This criterion has been adopted, for example, in the design of the ARPA computer network. What properties does this force on the network? The minimal network which satisfies this criterion is the *two-regular* network, which has exactly two arcs entering and two arcs leaving each node (fig. 6). Such a network is relatively inexpensive to install and yet is reliable in the sense that loss of a single information-transfer channel does not disrupt the network.

Any realistic network combines the features of each of these "pure" types. For example, one might want PLAN to look like a decentralized network within each of several regions—say,

within New England, the southeastern states, and along the Pacific coast. Between these decentralized subnets, one might want PLAN to be two-regular, or cyclic. Then, thinking in terms of state library networks associated with PLAN, one might want the network within each state to be hierarchical. However, at the present stage in modeling such a network, we find it exceedingly difficult to properly handle such a complex design. Thus, we restrict our attention to the four pure types defined above. It should be noted, however,

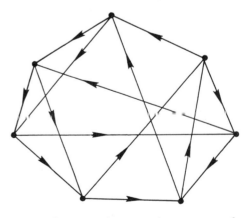

FIG. 6.—A two-regular network on seven nodes

that the general concepts which we define are valid for all networks.

GRAPH CONNECTIVITY

One criterion which is generally placed on information networks, particularly those involving libraries, is that each user of the network must have access to each information resource within the network. (There may be security classifications or other restrictions which prevent a user from actually reaching a document, but there should be no such restrictions due to the network design.) This concept of *total accessibility* is related to the graph-theoretic concept of connectedness.

We say that a digraph is *weakly connected* if, disregarding the directions assigned to the arcs, given any two nodes, n_a and n_b, there is a chain of arcs leading from n_a to n_b (see fig. 7). If this is not the case and if there is at least one pair of nodes between which there is no such chain of arcs, we say that the digraph is disconnected. Since we are interested in indicating information flow by the directions assigned to the arcs, weak connectivity is not a sufficient concept for our information network.

We come closer to the desired con-cept of total accessibility if we require that the digraph be *unilaterally connected*, that is, that between any two nodes, n_a and n_b, there be a chain of arcs which are consistently directed. Thus, we should be able to find a chain of directed arcs leading from n_a to n_b or a chain leading in the opposite direction (fig. 8). Unilateral connectivity provides a one-way path. We are able to get the request from the user to the library having the document, or we are able to get the document to the user, but not necessarily both. Clearly this is less than desirable: there is no sense in getting the request to the proper library if we cannot respond to that request. We need to strengthen the concept of connectivity still further. A digraph is *strongly connected* if, given any two nodes, n_a and n_b, there is a chain of arcs directed from n_a to n_b and another chain of arcs directed from n_b to n_a (see fig. 9). This is the connectivity definition which is needed to realize our concept of total accessibility. One chain of arcs takes the request message from the user at n_a to the library having the document, at n_b. The other chain of arcs returns the document to the user (fig. 10).

Returning briefly to the four types

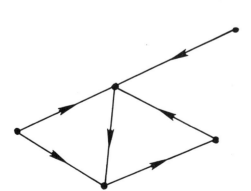

FIG. 7.—A weakly connected digraph

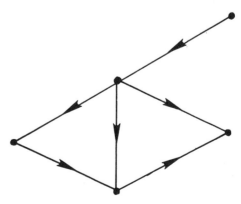

FIG. 8.—A unilaterally connected digraph

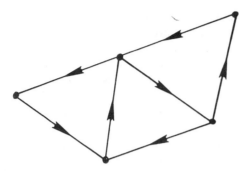

FIG. 9.—A strongly connected digraph

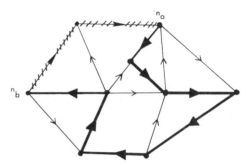

FIG. 10.—Information transfer paths from n_a to n_b and from n_b to n_a.

of networks which we have defined, the cyclic, decentralized, hierarchical, and two-regular, we see that each of these is, in fact, strongly connected. Moreover, if we construct a complex network using these four types as components, and if we insure that the components are at least cyclically connected among themselves, then we have a strongly connected network which is suitable for information transfer.

PARAMETERS FOR NETWORKS

This basic skeleton, the strongly connected digraph, is suitable for network design. However, we must associate with each node and each arc a host of parameters which define the properties applicable to the particular network. Certain of these parameters are associated primarily with the nodes (information centers). These include (1) the information media, (2) storage requirements, (3) access modes, (4) computer equipment, (5) volume of work load, (6) classification methods, (7) costs associated with the nodes, and (8) probability of servicing a request. While these parameters influence the operation of the network, we need not be concerned here with the precise manner in which this happens. The problem of adjusting these

parameter values is precisely the problem facing designers of libraries and other information centers. We assume that the nodes have certain characteristics, and then, in designing the network, we use the node characteristics as fixed values. Of course, changing the node characteristics requires redesign of the network.

Of more interest to us are the parameters which are associated primarily with the arcs of the network, that is, with the information-transfer channels rather than with the information centers. These parameters include (1) type of transfer, (2) volume of information, in terms of messages and documents, (3) permissible rates of transfer, (4) accuracy of transmission, (5) origin, (6) destination, and (7) cost of information transfer.

The information transfer may involve one of a number of different types of channels. These include messenger service, telephone calls, facsimile transmission, the mail, teletypewriter or other computer-terminal transmission, and so forth. Some types of transmission are more suited to the request message than to document transfer; others are equally suited to message and document transfer. One thinks of the typical request as being rather short, hence suitable for expensive high-speed transmission; while a document, being longer, is more suitable for slower, less-expensive transfer modes. The distinction between message and document transfer is stated in two previous papers [3, 4].

The volume of transactions to be conducted on the network also influences the design. Here again, one thinks of requests as being more frequent than documents in response to requests. This is partly true since the request may be replicated and sent to many parts of the network; but, generally, only a single copy of a responding document is required to be transferred.

Already we have alluded to the fact that there are both high-speed and low-speed modes of information transfer. Often one finds that a range of alternatives exists within a network for any single transfer. For example, a document in response to a request might be sent by facsimile, by messenger, or by mail. In actual operation, generally, limits are set on either response time or the cost of information transfer, or both. The origin and destination of information transfer over the network have a large influence on network design. As we mentioned above, the request message may be replicated and sent to all, or nearly all, information centers in the network. While union catalogs or switching centers may exist in some networks, often the user submitting the request does not know the location of the desired information. However, once the document is found, its destination, the user, is known. Thus, the transfer paths generated to send this document back to the user are far fewer in number than those necessary to handle the request message. And, of course, one of the problems of network design is that of the uneven distribution of users and documents within the network.

Finally, the cost of information transfer is a large factor in network design. Certainly, cost is interrelated with many other factors that we have mentioned, and it is entirely possible in an actual network to have parallel information-transfer channels at substantially different costs. Hopefully, a difference in service accurately reflects the cost difference.

While any comprehensive model must take into account all of the factors which we have discussed and other similar ones, in the present paper we wish to concentrate on the aspects of the problem which can be modeled by a digraph without including the various parameter values. In particular, we wish to define a measure and introduce two graphs derivable from any given graph; these help shed some light on the problems of network design.

NETWORK FLEXIBILITY

One measure which might be applied in judging a network design is the freedom of choice offered an information center in placing a request in the network. For example, a center in the cyclic network has no choice in the path by which it must route a request or in the path by which the response comes. There is only one path around the network. However, a center in the decentralized network has a great variety of paths available for the routing of request messages and document responses. Not only is there a direct connection from this information center to every other one, but also, in the event that one connection is broken, there are still a number of alternate routes. With this in mind, we define the *flexibility* of a network to be the quantity

$$F = \frac{Q - N}{N(N - 2)},$$

where Q is the number of arcs in the network, and N is the number of nodes. Note that since a cyclic network has $Q = N$, for such a network the flexibility is $F = F_c = 0$. Similarly, since a decentralized network has $Q = N(N - 1)$ arcs, for such a network the flexibility is $F = F_d = 1$. Continuing in the same vein, a hierarchical network has $Q = 2N - 2$ arcs, hence, a flexibility of $F = F_h = 1/N$; a two-regular network has $Q = 2N$ arcs, hence, a flexibility of $F = F_t = 1/(N - 2)$.

These flexibility calculations for the four special networks exhibit properties which are valid for any network. First, since the cyclic network has the minimum number of arcs for a given number of nodes and the decentralized network has the maximum number of arcs, it follows that for any network $0 \leqslant F \leqslant 1$. The values for F_h and F_t exhibit the following general property: if the number of arcs in a network is proportional to the number of nodes, then the flexibility varies inversely with the size of the network. In other words, if we set constant flexibility as a desirable criterion of network design, then, as we increase the size of the network, the number of arcs must increase more rapidly than the number of nodes—in fact, as the square of the number of nodes. For example, if we were to expand the PLAN network from forty-nine nodes to 490 nodes, then to maintain the flexibility we would need to increase the number of arcs 100-fold.

Let us now consider the two graphs derivable from a network which are of assistance in analyzing the network. The first of these defines, in some sense, the "core" of the network, while the second provides an overview. In many networks—for example, the hierarchical networks—we find that, in a portion of the network, arcs occur in antiparallel pairs. That is, we find an arc from n_a to n_b accompanied by one from n_b to n_a. Let us call the graph consisting of all such pairs of arcs the *two-skeleton* of the given network (fig. 11). In some sense, the two-skeleton represents the "core" or "spine" of the

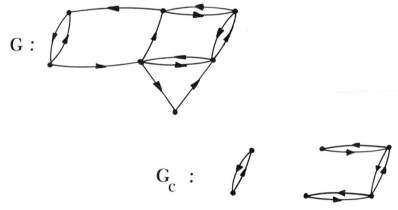

FIG. 11.—A network, G, and its two-skeleton, G_c

network, along which two-way communication is possible. Note that, for the decentralized network and the hierarchical network, the two-skeleton is the entire network; while, for the cyclic network on three or more nodes, the two-skeleton does not exist.

The other derived graph is the undirected graph obtained by removing all directions from the arcs of the network and identifying parallel edges (fig. 12). This graph, showing simply the connections existing throughout the network, is useful in determining connectivity and several other properties of the network, although by dropping the directionality of the arcs we do lose some network characteristics.

THE PURPOSE OF MATHEMATICAL MODELS

We might ask at this point, "Why the need for mathematical rigor?" This question is asked almost as frequently as the comment is made that "these problems cannot be solved by mathematics and models." Why, indeed, should we go to all the trouble of defining network models thoroughly and carefully? Why not merely assume that everyone knows what a library information network is and let it go at that? The answer lies in the removal of ambiguity by mathematical definition. One may disagree with the definitions, assumptions, and axioms that are stated; but, if the mathematics is correct, one cannot disagree with the conclusions developed from these definitions, assumptions, and axioms. One can, of course, offer different definitions and assumptions and observe their effect on the resulting conclusions. In such a way, one can compare different models or the same model as applied to different networks. The flexibility measure is a good example of this. One may argue that this measure is not the correct one and offer alternatives. But, assuming that the measure is at least reasonable, one can then draw, as we have, firm conclusions about the characteristics of networks according to the measure.

To the comment on the inadequacy of mathematics, we must agree that mathematics can neither describe nor solve *all* problems associated with information networks. *But neither can any other empirical or analytical technique.* Where applicable, mathematical models should be employed to describe and/or solve network problems amenable to mathematical solution. The modeler must accept the responsibility of stating the premises on which his model is built and conveying the implications of the conclusions that follow. In such a spirit we have conducted this work.

THE GENERAL NETWORK MODEL

We have discussed a number of different concepts—the pure types of networks, the ideas of connectivity, and the parameters associated with a network. We now present a general model which brings together these concepts. We define an *information network N* as a sextuple

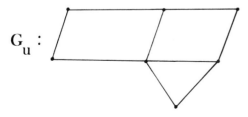

G_u :

FIG. 12.—G_u, the undirected graph corresponding to G of fig. 11.

$$N = U, I, C, A, \mathfrak{f}, \mathfrak{f}',$$

where the components of N are defined as below. The sets U, I, and C are the nodes of the network, representing the *users, information resources,* and *information centers,* respectively. We require that, with each information center $c \in C$, there be associated a nonempty set $U \subset U$ of users or a nonempty set $I \subset I$ of information resources, or both. The A is the set of directed arcs on $U \cup I \cup C$, where an arc (n_a, n_b) denotes that node n_b is directly accessible from node n_a, and where each arc (n_a, n_b) joining nodes of C carries one or both of the labels: m, denoting possible *message* (request) transfer from n_a to n_b; or d, denoting possible *document* (response) transfer from n_a to n_b. Thus, in a typical network, each user $(u \in U)$ has direct access to one or more information centers, and each information resource $(i \in I)$ is accessible to one or more centers. Note that no two users are directly connected: they must communicate via one or more centers. Similarly, no two information resources are directly connected.

The central portion of the network represents the connections between the information centers. It is this portion which really interests us. Within the central portion of the network, each arc carries one or both of the labels m and d. The arcs labeled m denote channels along which messages or requests for information may be passed. These arcs and their associated nodes form a digraph, G. In the light of our earlier discussion we assume that G be strongly connected, that is, that there be at least one message channel from any given center to any other given center.

Similarly, the arcs labeled d denote channels along which documents or re-

sponses to requests may be passed. As noted earlier, these channels may not coincide with the m-labeled channels. The digraph G' formed by the d-labeled arcs and their associated nodes is also required to be strongly connected. Thus, the central portion of our network model, which relates to the information centers, is covered by two strongly connected digraphs, G and G'.

These two digraphs covering C may be any of the pure types which we have discussed or they may be more complex digraphs. For example, G might be hierarchical, requiring that a request filter gradually up through the network until it can be satisfied. At the same time, G' might be decentralized, so that the document selected in response to a request can be sent directly to the center originating the request.

We have yet to explain the last two components of N, namely, f and f'. These are mathematical functions that define the *information-transfer structure* of the network. Note that, since the graph associated with N is strongly connected, any user can access any information resource. But we are interested in *how* this is accomplished. We wish to be able to compare the costs associated with various modes of access.

Within the digraph G, one can define several open paths, that is, consistently directed sequences of arcs which do not pass through any one node more than once. Given a user $u \in U$ attempting to access an information resource $i \in I$, we are interested in the set of all open paths P enabling this access. For each path $p \in P$, the value of $f(P)$ is the set of all ordered pairs (u, i), where $u \in U$ and $i \in I$ are joined by the path $p \in P$. Thus, $f(P)$ defines the paths that can be taken by a user in order to access specific information in the network. Note that all arcs of P are labeled m.

The function f' is similarly defined for paths P' (consisting of d-labeled arcs) in the digraph G'. Thus, f determines the alternatives for message or request flow, while f' determines the alternatives for document or response flow.

This, then, is our general network model—a model which embodies the concepts of the user, the information center, the information resource; the ideas of message and document flow; and functions defining the information-transfer structure for the network. From this basic structure, we may proceed in a number of directions. We certainly want to vary the central network structure. In fact, it appears useful to classify networks according to the G, G' structure, as shown in figure 13.

Furthermore, we wish to attach to the network model some or all of the parameters which we have discussed and to investigate the relationships among these. For any given assignment of parameter values, we find a "topography" for the network—information which is available to the user at various cost levels, $c_1 < c_2 < c_3 \ldots$. Such topographies help us define and study the fine structure of information networks and refine our concepts and modeling techniques so that we may easily and accurately model the large library networks necessary to handle today's information flow.

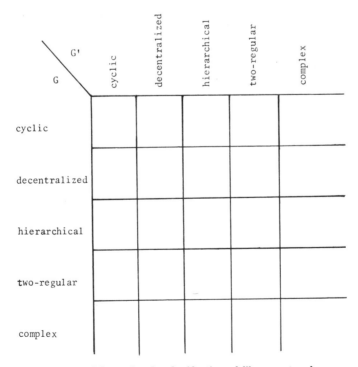

Fig. 13.—Schema for the classification of library networks

REFERENCES

1. Harary, Frank. *Graph Theory*. Reading, Mass.: Addison-Wesley Publishing Co., 1969.

2. Harary, Frank; Norman, Robert Z.; and Cartwright, Darwin. *Structural Model: An Introduction to the Theory of Directed Graphs*. New York: John Wiley & Sons, 1965.

3. Nance, Richard E. "An Analytical Model of a Library Network." *Journal of the American Society for Information Science* 21 (January–February 1970): 58–66.

4. Nance, Richard E.; Korfhage, Robert R.; and Bhat, U. Narayan. "Information Networks: Definitions and Message Transfer Models." Technical Report CP-710011. Dallas, Tex.: Computer Science/Operations Research Center, Southern Methodist University, July 1971.

MATHEMATICAL PROGRAMMING MODELS AND METHODS FOR THE JOURNAL SELECTION PROBLEM

FRED GLOVER AND DARWIN KLINGMAN

ABSTRACT

New model formulations and solution methods are given for the Journal Selection Problem discussed by Leimkuhler and studied by Kraft and Hill. This problem, whose significance for library operations has been noted by Raffel and Shisko, Morse, and others, is shown to be susceptible to formulation as a "multiple-choice" model that has advantages over previous formulations for determining the analytical implications of the model and for implementing a variety of solution approaches. The solution methods presented here are based on new procedures for applying surrogate constraints and dynamic programming. Our results are developed in a framework that can also accommodate problems with a somewhat different structure than the Journal Selection Problem, thus providing new solution strategies for these problems as well. Finally, we examine special structural assumptions that permit this model to be transformed into generalized and classical transportation models. Additional constraining relations relevant to the library setting are also discussed.

INTRODUCTION

The problem of selecting scientific journals, as discussed by Leimkuhler [1] and Williams, Bryant, Wiederkehr, and Palmour [2], has received considerable attention for its significance in applications of operations research to library decision making. Fundamentally, the model seeks to determine the optimal allocation of present and future (expected) funds to purchase scientific journals, using an objective function based on expected usage as a measure of journal worth. The importance of this problem in library management is examined in [3–6], and an excellent review of this literature, together with "suboptimal" methods for solving the Journal Selection Problem, appear in Kraft and Hill [7, 8].

The purpose of this paper is fourfold:

1. To indicate an alternative mathematical formulation of the Journal Selection Problem that has advantages over the formulation of [1, 7] for determining the analytical implications of the model and for implementing a variety of solution approaches.

2. To identify realistic parameter assumptions that will reduce the model to a special mathematical structure amenable to efficient solution techniques. In particular, parameter assumptions are discussed which permit the model to be solved by employing highly efficient solution procedures for solving transportation and generalized transportation problems [9–18].

3. To identify and extend the model to accommodate additional constraining relations that are relevant to the library setting.

4. To specify new solution methods (capable of solving the extended models as well as the original model) based on surrogate constraints and dynamic programming, significantly extending the range of problems for which "suboptimal" solutions are indeed optimal.

MATHEMATICAL FORMULATION

The Journal Selection Problem as discussed in [1, 7, 8] is formulated as a 0–1-integer-programming problem as follows:

Let $Y_{j,q-p,p}$ be a binary-valued variable which assumes the value one if the library has acquired as of period q the issues of journal j published in period p (hence, holds them at a time $q - p$ units after their publication and continues to hold them for all subsequent periods), and zero if the library has not acquired these issues. It is assumed that all variables relate to an action as of the end of a specific acquisition period, $q = 0, 1, 2, \ldots, r$, and that the acquisition can apply to a journal published in any period p ranging over $p = 0, 1, 2, \ldots, q$. Furthermore, the index j denotes a specific journal from a set of s journals (that is, $j = 1, 2, \ldots, s$) which contains all journals that are being considered by the library. Defining $G_{j,q-p,p}$ as the worth of acquiring as of period q the issues of journal j published in period p,[1] the objective becomes that of maximizing

$$Z = \sum_{j=1}^{s} \sum_{q=0}^{r} \sum_{p=0}^{q} (Y_{j,q-p,p} \, G_{j,q-p,p}),$$

subject to the constraints

$$Y_{j,q-p,p} = 0 \text{ or } 1$$
$$\text{for all } j, q, \text{ and } p. \qquad \text{(a)}$$

$$Y_{j,q-p,p} \geq Y_{j,q-p-1,p}$$
$$\text{for } j = 1, \ldots, s; \quad q = 0, \ldots, r; \qquad \text{(b)}$$
$$\text{and } p = 0, \ldots, q - 1$$

(expressing the fact that once an item is acquired it becomes a permanently maintained acquisition within the library system).

where $b_q =$ the budget for period q for use in the acquisition of new journals and maintenance of the collection of journals; $C_1 =$ the cost of initially adding the issues of a journal to the collection, excluding subscription cost; $C_2 =$ the periodic storage and recurring costs, including some allotment for expected replacement of lost, stolen, or defaced items; $C_3 =$ the cost per expected use of an item for circulation; $\lambda_{j,q-p,p} =$ expected use in period q of journal j published in period p; $K_{j,q-p,p}$ = the subscription cost to acquire the issues of journal j published in period p if acquired in period q.

The implications of this model and alternative approaches for solving it are discussed in [7, 8]. These previous solution approaches, as well as new ones proposed here, will be described in subsequent sections. However, we shall first provide an alternative formulation of the Journal Selection Problem which permits all of these approaches to be implemented more efficiently and which also permits the underlying model to be analyzed in a more convenient fashion.

A SIMPLIFIED FORMULATION

A shortcoming of the formulation indicated in the preceding section is the rather elaborate set of interconnections imbedded in the constraints (c) which are occasioned by the "precedence relations" among the variables given by (b). To eliminate these complexities and to produce a coefficient

$$\sum_{j=1}^{s} \sum_{p=0}^{q} Y_{j,q-p,p} \, (C_1 + C_2 + C_3 \lambda_{j,q-p,p} + K_{j,q-p,p})$$
$$- \sum_{j=1}^{s} \sum_{p=0}^{q-1} Y_{j,q-p-1,p} \, (C_1 + K_{j,q-p,p}) \leq b_q \text{ for } q = 0, \ldots, r, \qquad \text{(c)}$$

[1] Various possibilities for the coefficients $G_{j,q-p,p}$ of the objective function to reflect the goals of the library are discussed in [7].

matrix which is more amenable to analytical investigation, consider replacing the variables $Y_{j,q-p,p}$ by new variables x_{jpq} $(q \geq p)$ defined by x_{jpq} = 1 if the issue of journal j published in period p is *first acquired* in period q; and $x_{jpq} = 0$, otherwise. To represent the fact that a particular issue of a journal can be "first acquired" only once, it is then possible to write

$$\sum_{q \geq p} x_{jpq} \leq 1$$

(1)

for each j,p.

The assumption that a particular issue, once obtained, is maintained thereafter (over the planning horizon) can be accommodated by introducing the budget constraints,

$$\sum_{\substack{j,p,q: \\ p \leq q \leq h}} a_{jpq}^h x_{jpq} \leq b_h$$

(2)

for each period h, where the coefficient a_{jph}^h represents the cost of acquiring the "issue jp" in period h, and is thus given by

$$a_{jph}^h = C_1 + C_2 + C_3 \lambda_{jpq}^h + K_{jpq}^h,$$

and where the coefficient a_{jpq}^h for $q < h$ represents the cost of maintaining "issue jp" in period h, after having acquired it in period q, and is given by

$$a_{jpq}^h = C_2 + C_3 \lambda_{jpq}^h.$$

(Following the obvious convention, we have $\lambda_{jpq}^h \equiv \lambda_{j,q-p,p}$ and $K_{jpq}^h \equiv K_{j,q-p,p}$ for $\lambda_{j,q-p,p}$ and $K_{j,q-p,p}$, as defined previously.)

A clearer understanding of this alternative formulation can be gained by examining the structure of its coefficient matrix, which appears in table 1 for the case of 3 journals over three time periods (that is, j,p,q,h all range from 1 to 3, with $p \leq q \leq h$).[2]

Several things may be observed

about the structure of this model. First of all, the constraints of (1), which appear as the "top half" of the constraints in table 1, are of the "multiple-choice" variety which are susceptible to exploitation by generalized upper-bound techniques [19]. Such structures have been given special attention in the design of commercial computer codes for large-scale integer programs by Beale [20, 21]; and new cutting techniques for taking advantage of these and related structures have recently been developed by Glover and Klingman [22, 23]. It may also be remarked that the suboptimal solution methods proposed by Kraft and Hill [7, 8] for the original formulation can be straightforwardly adapted to this alternative formulation, with a resultant decrease in computational effort at each step. Additional benefits of the alternative formulation arise by considering amended assumptions concerning the cost and budget relationships that apply in special situations, as we shall subsequently demonstrate.

Because of the potentially vast number of variables and constraints of the problem (although the alternative formulation involves fewer constraints than the original), and because of the customary computational difficulties associated with obtaining globally optimal solutions to integer programs of this size with existing algorithms, the attempt to develop suboptimal methods for obtaining "good" but not necessarily optimal solutions is a highly appropriate pursuit. The value of a suboptimal method is, of course, crucially dependent upon the goodness of the solutions obtained (that is, the extent to which they deviate from a global optimum).

---

[2] We are following the convention of starting all indexes at one rather than starting j at one and the others at zero, as in the previous formulation.

TABLE 1
Coefficient Matrix for a 3-Journal, 3-Period Problem*

	JOURNAL 1						JOURNAL 2						JOURNAL 3							
	Publication Period						Publication Period						Publication Period							
	1			2		3	1			2		3	1			2		3		
	111	112	113	122	123	133	211	212	213	222	223	233	311	312	313	322	323	333		
	1	1	1	.	.	.	.	.	.	.	.	.	.	.	.	.	.	.	≤	1
	.	.	.	1	1	.	.	.	.	.	.	.	.	.	.	.	.	.	≤	1
	.	.	.	.	.	1	.	.	.	.	.	.	.	.	.	.	.	.	≤	1
	.	.	.	.	.	.	1	1	1	.	.	.	.	.	.	.	.	.	≤	1
	.	.	.	.	.	.	.	.	.	1	1	.	.	.	.	.	.	.	≤	1
	.	.	.	.	.	.	.	.	.	.	.	1	.	.	.	.	.	.	≤	1
	.	.	.	.	.	.	.	.	.	.	.	.	1	1	1	.	.	.	≤	1
	.	.	.	.	.	.	.	.	.	.	.	.	.	.	.	1	1	.	≤	1
	.	.	.	.	.	.	.	.	.	.	.	.	.	.	.	.	.	1	≤	1
α^1	α^1	.	.	.	.	.	α^1	.	.	.	.	.	α^1	.	.	.	.	.	≤	b_1
β^2	β^2	α^2	.	α^2	.	.	β^2	α^2	.	α^2	.	.	β^2	α^2	.	α^2	.	.	≤	b_2
β^3	β^3	β^3	α^3	β^3	α^3	α^3	β^3	β^3	α^3	β^3	α^3	α^3	β^3	β^3	α^3	β^3	α^3	α^3	≤	b_3

The first nine rows are the "Multiple-Choice" constraints; the last three rows (b_1, b_2, b_3) are the Budget constraints.

* The a_{jpq}^{h} coefficients are denoted by a_{jpq}^{h} when $h = q$ and by β_{jpq}^{h} when $q < h$. The subscripts associated with the a's and β's are indicated at the top of each column.

In the following, we shall propose suboptimal methods that can be demonstrated to provide globally optimal solutions under broader ranges of conditions than the methods previously developed for the Journal Selection Problem and, hence, whose suboptimal solutions have a greater likelihood of lying in the vicinity of the global optimum. To provide a framework for discussing these new methods and for indicating their relationship to earlier work, we shall first describe the previous suboptimal solution procedures proposed for this problem by Kraft and Hill.

THE METHODS OF KRAFT AND HILL

Kraft and Hill have proposed two suboptimal methods for the Journal Selection Problem which we describe here in terms of the formulation introduced in the second section above. The first [7] involves looking at each of the budget constraints of (2) in succession as if it were the only constraint of the problem. Upon examining the single budget constraint associated with period K, only the decision variables x_{jpq} are considered for which $q = K$ (that is, whose coefficients are represented by α^K in table 1). An optimal solution is then obtained to each of these "single-constraint integer programs" by the standard dynamic-programming recursion for the 0–1 knapsack problem. (Note that the constraints of [1] become redundant relative to the variables x_{jpK} for a given period K and, thus, do not affect the restricted knapsack problems.) Once an optimal solution is obtained to the knapsack problem associated with one budget period, this solution is then *enforced* for all subsequent periods by appropriately reducing the budget resources (the b_h coeffi-

cients) for these periods to account for the portion of the budget resources consumed as a result of setting particular variables equal to one. Correspondingly, for each variable x_{jpK} set equal to one, all of its "companion variables" x_{jpq} (for j and p fixed, and $q \neq K$) are permanently set equal to zero, thus assuring that none of the multiple-choice constraints will be subsequently violated. (This, of course, further restricts the variables that are free to be considered in solving subsequent knapsack problems.) In case the optimal knapsack solution uses more of the budget resource of a later period than is available for that period (by reducing the "current" b_h coefficient to less than zero), then Kraft and Hill sequentially select variables assigned a unit value in the knapsack solution and change their values to zero until all resource constraints are once again satisfied. At this point, the knapsack problem associated with the next budget constraint is examined (inheriting the reduced resource availabilities and restricted values of the problem variables), whereupon the process repeats until all budget constraints are exhausted. The final solution is guaranteed to be feasible but, of course, not necessarily optimal.

The second solution approach proposed by Kraft and Hill [8] makes use of the "generalized Lagrange" or "Everett" multiplier approach [12] which assigns nonnegative penalties to the budget constraints and then incorporates them into the objective function. The resulting "substitute problem" requires the maximization of the new function, subject only to the multiple-choice constraints. Because of the extremely simple form of this problem, the optimal solution can immediately be obtained by inspection (by examining the multiple-choice constraints one at a time and assigning a value of one to the variable of each constraint with the largest objective-function coefficient —unless this objective-function coefficient is negative, in which case all variables of the constraint are set equal to zero). To obtain an improving succession of substitute problems, the multipliers attached to the constraints are amended according to the prescription of Brooks and Geoffrion [24], using linear programming.

There is no guarantee that an optimal solution to the original problem will ever be obtained, but Kraft and Hill propose that interim feasible solutions be generated in a manner analogous to that of their first method.

LIMITING ASSUMPTIONS AND
EQUIVALENCES TO GENERALIZED
TRANSPORTATION PROBLEMS

To provide an estimate of the potential of their first method to obtain good solutions, Kraft and Hill indicate certain coefficient conditions under which this approach may be expected to do particularly well. It is possible to show that their algorithm may obtain nonoptimal solutions under the specified conditions, but the assumptions underlying these coefficient conditions can be exploited to advantage by alternative procedures that we shall now specify.

The three parameter assumptions analyzed by Kraft and Hill are as follows (see [7] for a discussion of the significance of these assumptions):

$$C_2 = C_3 = 0; \qquad \text{(i)}$$

$$C_3 = 0 \text{ and } K^h_{jpq} = K_h \text{ for all } j, p, q; \qquad \text{(ii)}$$

$$\lambda^h_{jpq} = \lambda_h, \text{ and } K^h_{jpq} = K_h \text{ for all } j, p, q. \qquad \text{(iii)}$$

As pointed out in [7], the consequence of assumption (i) is to break the link between the budget constraints. To verify this, observe that the coefficient values of the alternative formulation become:

$$a^h_{jpq} \equiv \alpha^h_{jpq} = C_1 + K^h_{jph}, \text{ if } q = h; \qquad \text{(a)}$$

$$a^h_{jpq} \equiv \beta^h_{jpq} = 0, \text{ if } q < h. \qquad \text{(b)}$$

By referring to table 1, it may be seen that the "direct" links between the budget constraints have been broken. From this observation, it is quite plausible to suppose that the "successive knapsack approach" of [7] will yield an optimal solution to this problem. Unfortunately, this is not the case. In fact, the successive knapsack approach may fail to obtain an optimal solution even when all of the budget constraints are completely redundant, as may be illustrated in a simplified manner by applying this approach to the problem: Maximize

$$3y_1 + 9y_2 + 1y_3 + 2y_4,$$

subject to

$$y_1 + y_2 \qquad \leqslant 1$$

$$y_3 + y_4 \leqslant 1$$

$$y_j = 0 \text{ or } 1, j = 1, 2, 3, 4,$$

where y_1 and y_3 are the variables of the first redundant knapsack constraint (not shown) and y_2 and y_4 are the variables of the second redundant knapsack constraint. The successive knapsack approach prescribes the solution $y_1 = 1$, $y_3 = 1$ to the first knapsack problem, forcing $y_2 = y_4 = 0$ and thus completing an assignment of values to all of the problem variables (leaving no free variables in the second knapsack problem). On the other hand, the optimal solution is obviously obtained by setting $y_2 = y_4 = 1$.

Taking a different tack and examining assumption (i) more closely within the framework of the formulation of the second section discloses that this assumption gives rise to an interesting model structure. Namely, one obtains an echelon-diagonal structure, corresponding to each publication period, where the entries on the echelon are 1, and the entries on the diagonal are $a_{jph}^h = \alpha_{jph}^h = C_1 + K_{jph}^h$. In general, this model structure (removing the integer requirements on the problem variables) is referred to as a generalized transportation [9–11, 18], for which efficient solution procedures exist [9, 13, 15]. Under certain circumstances, a_{jph}^h for all j,p,h can be scaled to one without altering the ones on the echelon, producing the model structure of the classical transportation (distribution) problem. For instance, if we assume $K_{iph}^h = K_h$ for all j,p (that is, all subscription costs in a given period are assumed the same), the coefficients in each budget constraint are equal to $C_1 + K_h$. Consequently, by dividing budget constraint h by $C_1 + K_h$, the coefficients on the echelons become equal to one.

The advantages of converting this model into a transportation problem are twofold:

1. If the right-hand side (RHS) coefficients of a transportation problem are integer valued, the optimal solution to the continuous problem with non-negativity constraints on the decision variables will always be integer valued. Because the decision variables in the Journal Selection Model are 0–1 variables, we can assume without loss of generality that the RHS coefficients of the "converted" problem are integer

valued. In view of the form of the multiple-choice constraints, an optimal solution to the converted problem (disregarding the 0–1 constraints) will still yield 0–1 values for the decision variables and will thus be optimal.

2. Highly efficient solution techniques exist for solving transportation problems. For instance, recent computational results reported in [25] indicate that it is possible to solve a transportation problem having 10,000 variables in less than 5 seconds on a CDC 6600 computer.

Consequently, assumptions which allow the model to be transformed into a transportation problem yield a problem that can be solved rapidly and also provide an *optimal* solution to the Journal Selection Problem. Some assumptions which allow the model to be transformed into a transportation problem are:

a) Assumption (ii) of Kraft and Hill [7] if, in addition, it is assumed that the budget constraints are equality constraints.

b) Assumption (iii) of [7] if, in addition, it is assumed that the budget constraints are equality constraints.

c) Assumption (i) of [7] if, in addition, it is assumed that $K_{jpq}^h = K_h$ for all j,p,q.

d) $C_2 = \lambda_{jpq}^h = 0$ for all j,p,q,h; and $K_{jpq}^h = K_h$ for all j,p,q.

Under the assumptions (*a*) and (*b*), the coefficients are $a_{jph}^h \equiv \alpha_{jph}^h = \alpha_h$ and $a_{jpq}^h \equiv \beta_{jpq}^h = \beta_h$. The model is transformed into a transportation problem by performing the following operations: (1) set $i = 1$; (2) divide the *i*th budget constraint by α_i; (3) successively subtract a β_h multiple of this altered budget constraint from the other budget constraints for $h = i + 1$,

..., r; and (4) if $i = r$, stop. Otherwise, set $i = i + 1$, and return to (2).

The transformation of the model in a transportation problem using assumptions (c) and (d) simply involves dividing the h budget constraint by α_h for $h = 1, 2, \ldots, r$.

It is important to note that, for cases in which the assumptions that permit the problem to be reduced to a transportation problem are not strictly valid, it may nevertheless be possible to approximate the original problem by one or several such transportation problems and to use the solutions thus obtained as starting solutions for procedures discussed in later sections.

SURROGATE-CONSTRAINT AND DYNAMIC-PROGRAMMING-SOLUTION METHODS

The approach to the Journal Selection Problem that we propose in this section combines dynamic-programming and surrogate-constraint concepts to provide a more effective substitute problem than in the successive Knapsack and generalized Lagrange multiplier approaches and also gives an efficient way of solving this new substitute problem. The surrogate-constraint strategy consists of replacing (or augmenting) a specified set of inequality constraints with one or more nonnegative linear combinations of these constraints. The new constraints thus created are regarded as "surrogates" for the original constraints to be used in guiding the progress of an appropriately designed problem-solving method. In the simplest version of this strategy, where a set of constraints is replaced by a single new constraint, the surrogate-constraint approach can be viewed as a generalization of the generalized Lagrange multiplier approach. Indeed, as shown by Greenberg and Pierskalla [26], the use of a surrogate constraint in place of the penalty function of the generalized Lagrange multiplier approach results in a smaller duality gap—that is, admits a wider range of circumstances under which an optimal solution to the substitute problem is also optimal to the original.

Procedures for generating strongest surrogate constraints for integer programming (according to a variety of definitions of "strongest") are given in Glover [27] and will not be discussed here. Such procedures can be applied adaptively in a manner analogous to those for obtaining amended values for generalized Lagrange multipliers and thus give rise to solution strategies resembling (but stronger than) those of the penalty-function approaches, provided it is possible to specify an efficient algorithm for the substitute problem containing the surrogate constraint.

To this end, we will show how to specify such an algorithm for the Journal Selection Problem when the budget constraints are aggregated into a single surrogate constraint and the multiple-choice constraints are left intact. The full influence of the multiple-choice constraints is thus taken into consideration in a global manner; and, consequently, the method avoids the pitfall illustrated in the preceding section, whereby nonoptimal solutions may be obtained even when the budget constraints are redundant.

The basis for our method for solving the surrogate problem is given by the following development, which provides an efficient dynamic-programming procedure for a more-general problem than that arising from the Journal Selection Problem.

Consider the problem (3). Maximize

$$\sum_{j\epsilon N_1} c_j(x_j) + \sum_{j\epsilon N_2} c_j(x_j)$$

$$+ \ldots + \sum_{j\epsilon N_r} c_j(x_j), \quad (3.1)$$

subject to

$$\sum_{j\epsilon N_1} a_j(x_j) + \sum_{j\epsilon N_2} a_j(x_j)$$

$$+ \ldots + \sum_{j\epsilon N_r} a_j(x_j) \leqslant b, \quad (3.2)$$

and

$$x^1 \epsilon S_1, x^2 \epsilon S_2, \ldots, x^r \epsilon S_r, \quad (3.3)$$

where the sets $N_1, N_2, \ldots, N_r$ are pairwise disjoint, and x^p denotes the vector (x_j) $j \epsilon N_p$. In general, the $c_j(x_j)$ may be arbitrary nonlinear scalar-valued functions, and the $a_j(x_j)$ may be arbitrary nonlinear vector-valued functions. Similarly, the sets S_p are permitted to consist of any collection of vectors x^p. For practical purposes, however, it is useful to impose more stringent assumptions—such as, requiring the domain of $a_j(x_j)$ to consist of vectors with a small number of components (preferably only one or two) and similarly stipulating that the sets S^p contain only a small number of vectors. (These and other more restrictive assumptions automatically hold for the surrogate problem that arises in connection with the Journal Selection Problem.)

Associated with problem (3), we define the "stage k subproblem" $P_k(s)$ (with right-hand side s): Maximize

$$\sum_{j\epsilon N_1} c_j(x_j) + \ldots + \sum_{j\epsilon N_k} c_j(x_j),$$

subject to

$$\sum_{j\epsilon N_1} a_j(x_j) + \ldots + \sum_{j\epsilon N_k} a_j(x_j) \leqslant s$$

$$x^1 \epsilon S_1, \ldots, x^k \epsilon S_k.$$

The $P_k(s)$ is, of course, the same as the original problem except that k replaces r and s replaces b. The optimal objective-function value for $P_k(s)$ will be denoted by $f_k(s)$. Then we may state the following result.

Theorem.—The optimal solution to $P_k(s)$ is linked to the optimal solution to a stage $k-1$ subproblem by the relationship

$$f_k(s) = \underset{x^k \epsilon S_k}{\text{Max}} \{ f_{k-1}[s - \sum_{j\epsilon N_k} a_j(x_j)]$$

$$+ \sum_{j\epsilon N_k} c_j(x_j) \}$$

for $k = 1, \ldots, r$, where $f_0(s) = 0$ for all $s \geqslant 0$ and $f_0(s) = -\infty$ otherwise.

Proof.—First, note that the "initialization conditions" defining $f_0(s)$ correspond to creating a "stage k" subproblem defined by: maximize $c_0(x_0)$, subject to $a_0(x_0) \leqslant s$, where $c_0(x_0) = 0$ and $a_0(x_0) = 0$ for all x_0. Thus, augmenting each successive subproblem $P_k(s)$ by $c_0(x_0)$ and $a_0(x_0)$ leaves the set of optimal solutions and the value of $f_k(s)$ unchanged for each of these subproblems. Moreover, the initialization conditions clearly specify the optimal solution to $P_0(s)$ (following the convention whereby a problem with no feasible solution is assigned an objective function value of $-\infty$). Thus, it is only required to show that the indicated value of $f_k(s)$ is correct for an arbitrary $k \geqslant 1$, assuming that the value of $f_{k-1}(s)$ is correct for all s. This follows at once by noting that, for any given (constant-valued) x^k, the subproblem $P_k(s)$ reduces to the subproblem

$$P_{k-1}[s - \sum_{j\epsilon N_k} a_j(x_j)]$$

with the objective-function value of

this latter problem increased by the constant

$$\sum_{j \epsilon N_k} c_j(x_j).$$

(Note that, if the problem constraint [3.2] is an equality rather than an inequality, the theorem remains valid simply by changing the initialization conditions to $f_0(0) = 0$ and $f_0(s) = -\infty$ for $s \neq 0$.)

A SIMPLIFIED RECURSION

The foregoing theorem gives a convenient dynamic-programming recursion for solving problem (3) (which is just $P_r(b)$) whenever the constraints (3.2) and (3.3) have a tractable structure. In the context of the surrogate problem derived from the Journal Selection Problem, the constraints $x^k \epsilon S^k$ have the form

$$\sum_{j \epsilon N_k} x_j \leqslant 1,$$

with $x_j = 0$ or 1, $j \epsilon N_k$; and the functions $c_j(x_j)$ and $a_j(x_j)$ are simply scalar products of the form $c_j x_j$ and $a_j x_j$. Thus, the recursive formula reduces to specifying that $f_k(s)$ is the larger of $f_{k-1}(s)$ and

$$\underset{j \epsilon N_k}{\text{Max}}[f_{k-1}(s - a_j) + c_j].$$

This formula is clearly very efficient from a computational standpoint.

The optimal solution generated for $P_r(b)$ can be conveniently recovered using this formula by storing an index k^* for each $P_k(s)$, where k^* names an index $j \epsilon N_k$ at which the maximum defining $f_k(s)$ is achieved, or (by convention) $k^* = 0$ if $f_k(s) = f_{k-1}(s)$. Thus, upon identifying the index k^* for the problem $P_r(b)$, we immediately know which of the variables x_j, $j \epsilon N_r$ is set

equal to 1 (if any), and thereby can identify the subproblem $P_{r-1}(s)$ that results from $P_r(b)$ under this assignment. The same process serves to identify the optimal value for x_j, $j \epsilon N_k$, at each stage k, together with the appropriate stage $k - 1$ subproblem, by means of which the recovery process can continue.

IMPLEMENTING THE RECURSION

To implement the recursive formula requires the determination of an appropriate range for s at each stage. For discrete variable problems, it is natural to stipulate that $a_j(x_j)$ be integer valued and b equal an integer, which enables s to range over a set of consecutive integers (for example, from zero to b when the $a_j(x_j)$ are nonnegative, as in the present context). A simple way to handle this stipulation for the surrogate problem is to replace a_j by $[a_j/\lambda]$, and b by $[b/\lambda]$, where λ is positive and where the square brackets denote the largest integer $\leqslant$ the quantity inside. This corresponds to replacing the original inequality by a Gomory "all-integer" cut [27, 28]. The use of the substituted cut makes it possible to control the size of b in the resulting constraint (by the choice of λ), and thus to assure that the total computational effort will be confined to an acceptable range in the approaches that apply the recursive formula for all integers s from zero to b.

AN IMPROVED RANGE FOR s

We shall now propose an approach that makes it possible to apply the dynamic recursion to only a subset of the values of s from zero to b, thus admitting a wider range of cuts that can acceptably replace the original inequality as well as improving overall efficiency. For this purpose, we define

$$a_k^* = \text{Max} \ (a_j),$$
$$\qquad\qquad {}_{j \epsilon N_k}$$

$$u_k = \sum_{h=1}^{k} a_h^*,$$

$$v_k = \sum_{h=k+1}^{r} a_h^* \quad (v_r \equiv 0).$$

Then we stipulate that s be restricted at stage k to satisfy

$$\text{Max} \ (b - v_r, 0) \leqslant s \leqslant \text{Min} \ (u_r, b).$$

To verify the legitimacy of this restriction, note first that, if $u_r \leqslant b$, then the constraint involving b is completely redundant, and the optimal solution can be obtained by inspection in the manner described earlier. (This follows from the fact that $a_j \geqslant 0$ for all j in the problem under consideration.) Thus, we assume $u_r > b$, in which case the foregoing stipulation restricts s for the stage r subproblem to the interval $b \leqslant s \leqslant b$. Thus, $s = b$, which accords with the fact that $P_r(b)$ is the only problem whose solution is relevant at stage r. In general, for any stage k, $k < r$, if $s \leqslant b - v_k$, then the constraint involving b is redundant from stage $k + 1$ onward (given that only s units of b are consumed through stage k). From among all such s that provide a "redundant continuation," the best is, of course, the largest, or $s = b - v_k$, since this provides the largest objective-function value for the first k stages. This justifies the lower bound stipulated for s. On the other hand, for all $s \geqslant u_k$, the optimal solution to $P_k(s)$ must be the same as to $P_k(u_k)$, since all such s are redundant relative to the stage k subproblem—and hence there is no need to examine any values of s exceeding u_k.

TIGHTER BOUNDS FROM DOMINANCE CONSIDERATIONS

Additional tightening of the bounds on s and further reduction of the computational effort in applying the dynamic-programming recursion can be obtained by reference to the following dominance considerations. Specifically, if p and q are the two indexes that belong to the same set N_k, and if $c_p \geqslant c_q$ and $a_p \leqslant a_q$, then the variable x_q may be automatically set to zero and eliminated from further consideration. (If $c_p = c_q$ and $a_p = a_q$, ambiguity may be avoided by supposing p is the smaller index.) By the process of casting out such dominated variables, the values a_k^* may be appreciably reduced, thus leading to further restrictions on the range of s. The indicated dominance criteria are, of course, inapplicable if p and q do not belong to the same index set, for then it is conceivable that an optimal solution exists with both x_p and x_q equal to one.

GENERATING MORE THAN ONE SURROGATE CONSTRAINT

Using the fact that the theorem applies to multiple constraints as well as to one (viewing $a_j(x_j)$ as a vector-valued function), it is possible to take advantage of "strongest surrogate constraints" that are generated according to two different definitions (following [27]). Then, using cuts to keep the components of b (which is now a two-dimensional vector) within an acceptable range, the recursive formula may be applied to solve the resulting two-constraint problem. The restrictions on s indicated above can be modified by analogous reasoning to provide appropriate restrictions when s is a two-component vector. In general, since the recursive formula involves only as many stages as there are sets N_k (which are somewhat fewer than the number of problem variables), its use is ideally suited to the solution of large-scale problems.

SUBOPTIMAL SOLUTIONS FOR THE JOURNAL SELECTION PROBLEM

A variety of possibilities exist for applying the surrogate-dynamic-programming approach to obtain "good" feasible solutions to the Journal Selection Problem. A special feature of this approach is that, if an optimal solution to a surrogate problem is feasible for the Journal Selection Problem, then it is optimal for this latter problem as well, and nothing more needs to be done. (To take further advantage of this possibility, the record keeping of the dynamic-programming method can be amended to allow the recovery of alternative optima.)

In addition, the optimal solution to the surrogate problem provides an upper bound on the objective-function value for its parent problem, and thus yields a basis for gauging how far a suboptimal solution may deviate from a global optimum.

Anticipating the likelihood that the solution to the surrogate problem will not be feasible for the Journal Selection Problem, a more elaborate strategy is required. The approach of Kraft and Hill is highly useful in this regard, wherein variables that are assigned a unit value are allowed to be successively set to zero, with the assurance that a feasible solution will eventually be obtained. In particular, the method of [8] provides an especially ingenious scheme for gauging the effect of a changed assignment on the currently violated constraints. In a slightly broadened framework, this method may be viewed as an instance of a strategy that selects a variable to be set to zero by reference to the resulting reduction in a weighted sum of infeasibilities, attaching higher weights to infeasibilities associated with constraints that are more strongly violated. The effect of the objective function is taken into account by ranking the variables on the basis of ratios of their objective-function coefficients to the reductions in the weighted sums of infeasibilities. Once the solution has been restored to feasibility, a reverse strategy is applied to determine whether any variables currently zero may be increased to one.

We shall not attempt to expand upon the heuristic possibilities contained in this and related frameworks, since discussions of such considerations may be found elsewhere (see, for example, [29–32]). Instead, we turn our attention to a refinement of the surrogate-constraint approach that permits these considerations to be applied more effectively.

TRANSFORMED SURROGATES

We propose a new use of surrogate constraints that is designed to obtain solutions with an increased likelihood of being optimal for the original problem, thus providing a better starting point for the application of follow-up heuristics.

For this purpose, we introduce the notion of a *transformed surrogate problem,* based upon the solution to an original surrogate problem, as follows.

Let the Journal Selection Problem be written in the form: Maximize

$$\sum_{j \epsilon N_1} c_j x_j + \ldots + \sum_{j \epsilon N_r} c_j x_j,$$

subject to

$$\sum_{j \epsilon N_1} A_j x_j + \ldots + \sum_{j \epsilon N_r} A_j x_j \leqslant A_0$$

$$\sum_{j \epsilon N_p} x_j = 1$$

for $p = 1, \ldots, r$, and $x_j \geqslant 0$, and integer for all j.

The multiple-choice constraints have been written as equalities rather than inequalities in this formulation in order to simplify the following discussion. (Such an equality structure can always be created by the addition of slack variables.)

Suppose, now, that a surrogate problem has been formed from the preceding problem and yields the solution $x_{k*} = 1$, $k^* \epsilon N_k$; $x_j = 0$ for $j \neq k^*$, $j \epsilon N_k$, $k = 1, \ldots, r$. Assuming that this solution is infeasible for the Journal Selection Problem, consider the new problem. Maximize

$$\sum_{j \epsilon N_1} d_j x_j + \ldots + \sum_{j \epsilon N_r} d_j x_j,$$

subject to

$$\sum_{j \epsilon N_1} B_j x_j + \ldots + \sum_{j \epsilon N_r} B_j x_j \leqslant B_0,$$

$$\sum_{j \epsilon N_p} x_j = 1, \ p = 1, \ldots, r,$$

$$x_j \geqslant 0, \text{ and integer for all } j,$$

where

$$B_0 = A_0 - \sum_{k=1}^{r} A_{k*},$$

and for each $k = 1, \ldots, r$, $d_j = c_j - c_{k*}$, $B_j = A_j - A_{k*}$, for all $j \epsilon N_k$ (including $j = k^*$). This transformed problem is equivalent to the original as may be verified by noting that it can be constructed by solving for the variables x_{k*} in the multiple-choice constraints and substituting the resulting expressions in the remaining constraints. The significance of this transformation

is that it "installs" the solution to the surrogate problem as a coordinate origin (or advanced start) for the new problem. The methods of [27] may then be directly applied to obtain strongest surrogate constraints for the transformed problem (using definitions which assure that such constraints will not be satisfied by the solution to the previous surrogate problem). Each such constraint gives rise to a transformed surrogate problem which, in general, will not exhibit the convenient nonnegative coefficient property that made it easy to specify restrictive bounds on the range of s. However, this apparent disadvantage is readily circumvented. Because the dynamic-programming procedure fully accommodates all the constraints by means of which the transformed problem was created, an entirely equivalent approach is to return to the original problem and generate the surrogate constraint from multiples of its constraints identical to those that were applied to the constraints of the transformed problem. (We implicitly assume that the surrogates themselves are created without reference to the multiple-choice constraints.) Thus, the solution procedures previously described can be used without modification. It is to be noted that this transformed surrogate approach can be applied to solutions that are obtained heuristically as well as to those that are obtained by solving previous surrogate problems.

ADDITIONAL MODELS

Several additional constraining relations that are relevant to the library setting can be easily incorporated in the Journal Selection Model. For instance, it might be realistic to penalize future budgets in an amount equal to some portion of the unexpended budget in the preceding periods. Or it might be more realistic to allow a journal to be thrown out of the library to make money and space available for others. These and other extensions of the Journal Selection Model will be discussed in this section.

The Journal Selection Model assumes that the budget for each period q is equal to an amount b_q, whether the previous budgets were spent. When dealing with public and private enterprises, more realistic assumptions might be, respectively:

1. To reduce the budget in period $h + 1$ by an amount equal to some fraction of the budget not spent in period h.

2. To increase the budget in period $h + 1$ by an amount equal to some fraction of the unexpended budget in period h.

Both of these assumptions can be easily incorporated into the model by multiplying the slack variable associated with the budget constraint for period h, s_h, by some number c_h ($0 \leqslant c_h \leqslant 1$) and adding or subtracting, respectively, this product from the left-hand side of the $(h + 1)$st budget constraint. An analogous procedure could be used to adjust the budget of all subsequent periods (that is, periods $h + 2, h + 3, \ldots, r$) rather than adjusting only the immediately succeeding period's budget.

Another assumption of the journal selection model is that, once a journal is obtained, it is maintained thereafter over the planning horizon. It might be desirable, however, to eliminate a journal from the library in order to provide the money and space for other journals. This alternative can be easily provided for by introducing decision variables y_{jpt} which allow a journal to be dropped (that is, no longer maintained after n periods from the purchase period) from the library. Thus, the new variables y_{jpt} are defined by $y_{jpt} = 1$ if the issue of journal j, published in period p, and first acquired in period t is dropped from the library in period $t + n$; and zero, otherwise. (This pertains where t is restricted to the values $t = 1, 2, \ldots, r - n$ and $t \leqslant p$.) The coefficient associated with y_{jpt} in the h budget constraint is $-a^n_{jpt}$ if $t + n \leqslant h$; and zero, otherwise. The constraints $y_{jpt} \leqslant x_{jpt}$ for each j, p, t must be adjoined to the model in order to guarantee that a journal is not dropped which has not been purchased. The coefficient of the variable y_{jpt} in the objective function should reflect the expected loss of dropping these issues from the library.

Another limitation of the Journal Selection Model is that all possible journals to be considered for purchase during the planning horizon are assumed to be known. Such prescience scarcely seems realistic. Instead, it would seem desirable to make explicit allowance for the appearance of new journals that the library may wish to acquire.

One approach would be to set aside an arbitrary amount of each budget for the purchase of new journals. This approach, however, suffers from the obvious shortcoming of not allowing all decisions to be made interactively.

A preferable alternative is to create a new 0–1 decision variable x_h for each budget constraint h whose coefficient in this budget constraint is equal to the anticipated cost of purchasing and maintaining one (or more) new journals and whose coefficient in future budget constraints is equal to the anticipated cost of maintaining these journals. The coefficient of the variable x_h in the objective function should represent the expected worth to the library of possessing such journals.

Alternatively, one could create several new variables for each budget constraint, incorporating these variables in the multiple-choice constraints.

It should be noted that proposed surrogate-dynamic-programming approaches can be readily extended to handle problem structures more general than that of the original Journal Selection Problem and, thus, can accommodate considerations such as the foregoing without difficulty.

REFERENCES

1. Leimkuhler, F. F. "Storage Policies for Information Systems." Research Memorandum Series 69-8. Mimeographed. Lafayette, Ind.: School of Engineering, Purdue University, June 1969.
2. Williams, G.; Bryant, E. C.; Wiederkehr, R.; and Palmour, V. E. *Library Cost Models: Owning versus Borrowing Serial Publications.* Chicago: Center for Research Libraries, 1968.
3. Downs, R. B. "The Implementation of Book Selection Policy in University and Research Libraries." In *Selection and Acquisition Procedures in Medium-sized and Large Libraries,* edited by H. Goldkor. Champaign, Ill.: Illini-Union Bookstore, 1963.
4. Raffel, J. A., and Shiskko, R. *Systematic Analysis of University Libraries: An Application of Cost-Benefit Analysis to the M.I.T. Libraries.* Cambridge, Mass.: M.I.T. Press, 1969.
5. Meier, R. "Overload and Growth in Communications—Oriental Institutions." In *Mathematical Exploration in Behavior Science,* edited by F. Massarick and P. Ratoosk. Homewood, Ill.: Irwin & Dorsey Press, 1965.
6. Morse, P. *Library Effectiveness: A System Approach.* Cambridge, Mass: M.I.T. Press, 1968.
7. Kraft, D. H., and Hill, T. W. "The Journal Selection Problem in a University Library System." Research Memorandum Series, Technical Report. Mimeographed. Lafayette, Ind.: School of Industrial Engineering, Purdue University, 1971.
8. Kraft, D. H., and Hill, T. W. "A Lagrangian Formulation of the Journal Selection Model." Technical Report. Mimeographed. Lafayette, Ind.: School

of Industrial Engineering, Purdue University, 1971.
9. Balas, E., and Ivanescu (Hammer), P. "On the Generalized Transportation Problem." *Management Science* 1 (September 1964): 188–202.
10. Charnes, A., and Cooper, W. W. *Management Models and Industrial Applications of Linear Programming.* Vols. 1 and 2. New York: John Wiley & Sons, 1961.
11. Dantzig, G. B. *Linear Programming and Extensions.* Princeton, N.J.: Princeton University Press, 1963.
12. Everett, H., III. "Generalized Lagrange Multiplier Method for Solving Problems of Optimum Allocation of Resources." *Operations Research* 11 (1963): 399–417.
13. Glover, F.; Klingman, D; and Napier, A. "A One-Pass Algorithm to Determine a Dual Feasible Basic Solution for a Class of Capacitated Generalized Networks." Research Report, no. 42. Mimeographed. Austin: Center for Cybernetic Studies, University of Texas, October 1970. To appear in *Operations Research.*
14. Hadley, R. *Linear Programming.* Reading, Mass: Addison-Wesley Publishing Co., 1962.
15. Lorie, Janice. "Topology and Computation of the Generalized Transportation Problem." *Management Science* 2 (September 1964): 120–24.
16. Simonnard, Michel. *Linear Programming.* Translated by William S. Jewell. Englewood Cliffs, N.J.: Prentice-Hall, Inc., 1966.
17. Taha, H. A. *An Introduction to Operations Research.* New York: Macmillan Co., 1971.
18. Wagner, H. W. *Principles of Operations Research with Applications to Managerial*

Decisions. Englewood Cliffs, N.J.: Prentice-Hall, Inc., 1969.

19. Dantzig, G. B., and VanSlyke, R. M. "Generalized Upper Bounding Techniques." *Journal System Science* 1 (1968): 213–26.

20. Beale, E. M. L. "Selecting an Optimum Subset." In *Integer and Nonlinear Programming,* edited by J. Abadie. Amsterdam: North-Holland Publishing Co., 1970.

21. Beale, E. M. L. "Advanced Algorithmic Features for General Mathematical Programming Systems." In *Integer and Nonlinear Programming*, edited by J. Abadie. Amsterdam: North-Holland Publishing Co., 1970.

22. Glover, F., and Klingman, D. "The Generalized Lattice Point Problem." Research Report, no. 37. Austin: Center for Cybernetic Studies, University of Texas, March 1970.

23. Glover, F., and Klingman, D. "Concave Programming Applied to a Special Class of 0–1 Integer Problems." Working paper 69-30. Austin: University of Texas, January 1969. To appear in *Operations Research.*

24. Brooks, R., and Geoffrion, A. "Finding Everett's Lagrange Multipliers by Linear Programming." *Operations Research* 14 (1966): 1149–53.

25. Glover, F.; Karney, D.; Klingman, D.; and Napier, A. "A Comparison of Computational Times for Various Starting Procedures, Basis Change Criteria, and Solution Algorithms for Distribution Problems." Research Report, no. 43. Austin: Center for Cybernetic Studies, University of Texas, May 1971.

26. Greenberg, H. J., and Pierskalla, W. P. "Surrogate Mathematical Programs." *Operations Research* 18 (1970): 924–39.

27. Glover, F. "Surrogate Constraints." *Operations Research* 16 (1968): 741–49.

28. Glover, F. "Convexity Cuts and Cut Search." Management Science Report Series 70-2. Boulder: Graduate School of Business, University of Colorado, 1970. To appear in *Operations Research.*

29. Echols, R. E., and Cooper, L. "The Solution of Integer Linear Programming Problems by Direct Search." Report no. AM66-1. Saint Louis, Mo.: Department of Applied Mathematics and Computer Sciences, Washington University, 1966.

30. Glover, F. "Heuristics in Integer Programming. Paper read at Colloquium on Management Decision Making for Engineers, Lakeway, Tex., September 1967. Mimeographed. Austin: College of Business Administration, University of Texas, 1967.

31. Hillier, F. S. "Efficient Suboptimal Algorithms for Integer Linear Programming with an Interior." Technical Report, no. 2. Mimeographed. Palo Alto, Calif.: Stanford University, August 1966.

32. Reiter, S., and Reiter, S. "Discrete Optimizing." *Journal of the Society for Industrial and Applied Mathematics* 13 (June 1965): 864–89.

DIRECTORY DESIGN FOR NETWORKS OF INFORMATION AND REFERRAL CENTERS[1]

MANFRED KOCHEN

ABSTRACT

In the last few years, we have seen the very rapid, but surprisingly little publicized, growth of information and referral centers. These agencies, whose purpose is to help citizens with almost any question they may have, have been developing without careful planning. Operations research provides a means for assisting such planning. A model is presented that indicates the increase in use to be expected for a given level of service. Another model shows that a network of consultants can improve the performance of a single consultant, even if the single consultant is much more able than the others. The final model analyzes a directory to a data base and introduces the concept of "zoomability" as a means for improving directory performance. A computer program useful in designing directions for a network of consultants is described as an example of the tools provided by operations research.

INTRODUCTION

"My son has just been arrested. What do I do? Whom do I call?" Such was the request of a concerned mother calling a stranger who answered the telephone number she dialed. She believed, perhaps with a mixture of fear, hope, and skepticism, that the stranger would give her a helpful response.

Which number might the concerned mother have dialed? Those of "Action Line," the mayor's office, the local public library, or a special regional information service are all possibilities. There are many others. If the response from one of these proved helpful, she would be likely to call that number again when a similar problem arises.

The almost unnoticed appearance in the last few years of thousands of information and referral (I & R) centers which aim to help the citizens of a

community with any question they may have may betoken a significant new phenomenon with possibly revolutionary implications for the knowledge industry as a whole and library/information sciences in particular. The approach to problems in the reference department of a small special library, in an information center, or by a university professor acting as a consultant may not differ greatly in principle. Moreover, the conditions under which each of these agencies performs effectively and the ways of improving their cost-effectiveness may be the same.

To illustrate the similarities, consider how, as a member of a university computer committee acting in the role of a consultant, I might encounter the following question: "What is a cost-effective file search program for a laboratory data base in radiology?" I could provide a response which is (a) barely adequate, within minutes, by recall from my unaided memory; (b) fair, within hours, by searching my private files and personal libraries

[1] The assistance of A. Breveleri, R. Chlopan, and R. Crickman with the new programs and analysis reported in this paper was very valuable. This work was performed with the partial support of National Science Foundation grant GN 879.

which have become quite rich after years of research and study in this area; (c) better, within a day or two, by searching the local library system, and asking colleagues; (d) good, within a week or two, by calling or writing to more remotely located colleagues and libraries, using contacts in a *network* of which I am a part.

The last point, indicating that as a member of the academic community I am part of a network—indeed, of a net of several subnetworks—is crucial and applies almost equally to an I & R center. For were the question by the unfortunate mother addressed to me, I would probably have to select "barely adequate" from (a) and "by searching the local library system . . ." from (c) or "by calling or writing to more remotely located colleagues . . ." from (d). I would need to know where I could responsibly refer it.

My way of answering the inquiry resembles that of an I & R center. In both cases, the use of referral and reliance of the respondent as a node in a referral and information network is of great importance. A trend toward the consolidation of the great proliferation of Kruzas's new I & R centers into networks is beginning to be noticeable [1–4].

The network concept was greeted by the information science community with a mixed reaction, although it did make a definite impact. "Networking is not a fairytale" read a button given out by an exhibitor at a recent ALA conference, implying that some feel that networks are a myth. Others [5] searched for more precise conceptualizations as well as actualizations of library networks, and more sober and realistic appraisals of the potential value of networks appeared. The key

feature of a network is that it somehow exhibits "emergent" properties not possessed by any of its components. Presumably, library networks can bring library resources to bear on real problem solving in ways not possible without networks.

I argue in this paper that directories which reflect the organization of knowledge and are adapted to the needs and habits of their users are necessary for I & R centers with large data bases. They are even more necessary for enabling a net of such centers to help solve problems *not* solvable without networks. Operations research techniques are used to establish this argument and to analyze and design such directories.

CURRENT DEVELOPMENTS IN PROVIDING USEFUL INFORMATION SERVICES

Swank [6] regards an information network[2] as characterized by six parts:

1. *Information resources* or data bases. I modify this to read "distributed or scattered data bases," requiring special provisions for cross-talk and communication.

2. *Users,* usually remote from the service center. I will call them rooted users, because getting them to move more than 20 feet from their usual work place requires a leap in incentive.

3. *Schemes for the intellectual organization* of the resources, such as catalogs or directories. I prefer the broader term, directory, and stress its function as a device for actualizing the potential connections among a very great diversity of intellectual resources.

[2] I, like Swank, will use "information nets" and "library nets" as if they were synonyms, and intend both to focus on "networks of information and referral centers or of referential consultants."

4. *Methods for delivery.* I shall view these as members of a hierarchy of terminals, and procedures for using these terminals.

5. *Formal organization* of agencies in the net, to which I should like to add appropriate aspects of the informal organization. The nodes of the net are facilities for processing information, servicing requests, giving advice, referring, and also agencies to which referrals are made and which provide services other than informing.

6. *Teleprocessing facilities* which link the agencies or facilities to one another, to the users and to the data bases.

Swank recognizes the third part to be of central concern, as the "really unique, gut problem of any library or information service." He postulates that the selectivity required in the intellectual-logical organization of a data base through directories varies in direct proportion to the size of the data base. We must ask How can a directory provide the necessary selectivity, sensitivity, flexibility, reactivity? How can we compare two directories with respect to these properties? How can we select or design a good directory which enables the service of a network to actually "reach" its users and provide them with useful responses to real needs?

Large institutions in the knowledge industry [7] have for some time fielded almost any question reaching them by mail, telephone, or face-to-face contact. The Library of Congress, the *New York Times,* and Time, Incorporated each responds to well over 100,000 requests per year. Generally, the nontrivial questions for these institutions pertain to the use and content of that part of its files not readily available

elsewhere. The offices of the mayors in at least two large cities, New York City and Philadelphia, get as many as 700 inquiries per day, usually pertaining to the daily needs of citizens.

Many writers on librarianship draw careful distinctions between libraries, information centers, question-answering services, and information and referral centers. But since more and more small community libraries seem to be answering citizens' questions or referring inquiries, a trend may well be developing among librarians toward recognizing and meeting the need for information and referral services [4, 8–10].[3] We now consider such agencies.

One of the first of these services was the Citizens' Advice Bureau started in the United Kingdom during World War II [11]. These fielded over a million inquiries per year between 1961 and 1965, mostly about family and personal matters. One variant of this, the Neighborhood Information Center (NIC), was proposed for adaptation to needs in the United States in 1966. Three of the most striking conclusions resulting from the NIC's operations were (1) that nearly half the people requiring an existing service don't know of its existence, and neither do professionals in the social service system; (2) that there is an almost inverse relation between intensity of need and ease of access; and (3) that there is a lack of flexible responsiveness by existing agencies to diverse local conditions.

Over 3,000 agencies providing in-

[3] In a private communication in 1970, Prof. C. Bunge, of the University of Wisconsin, called my attention to the work of S. Rothstein in developing such an expanded notion of reference librarianship.

formation and referral service exist to-day, and the number of new agencies introduced each year seems almost to have been doubling for the past few years [12]. According to Long et al., a typical information and referral center lies in a community of about 100,000, is about five years old, is part of a larger organization, is run by a professional in social work, is staffed by two professionals and a secretary, provides information about very specialized services offered by over fifty agencies to which clients may be referred, and handles about 290 telephone inquiries per year per 100,000 population. The average budget may be about $25,000 per year, and despite absence of follow-up data, over half of the inquiries are believed to be serviced satisfactorily.

Many of the problems of analyzing such a service lend themselves to the methods of operations research. Judicious choice and handling of the problems can make a significant impact on the further development of such information and referral centers. Let us analyze two such problems in more detail. We use the North Philadelphia Model Cities Information Center (MCIC)[4] as a vehicle.

The above-mentioned referral service was initiated by Ball [13] and can be regarded as a pilot model. It began serving a population of about 200,000 on November 9, 1970. The staff of about thirty model cities personnel includes eight information and referral (I & R.) specialists who answer telephone inquiries and four librarians. Telephones are answered from 8:30 A.M. to 5 P.M. and a tape answering

service is on the rest of the time. The MCIC uses three-way telephone hook-ups; the client hears his case being discussed or referred to a third party, possibly a social service agency that might help him. The I & R specialists listen for a while to check whether the contact made between the third party and the client is satisfactory; if not, he switches the client to another, more appropriate "third" party. Over 95 percent of the information requests are handled similarly, although some can drag on over weeks.

The MCIC has a potential of servicing about 150 requests per day, but received only about fifty cases per day in June 1971. Despite its impressive growth from zero cases per day in November 1970, the MCIC director, J. Ball, considers the first of his key problems to be that of reaching still more citizens. He wants them to realize that this service exists, and will take on any kind of problem. The service load in cases per day is viewed as a performance measure. Operations research can be expected to give some insights, as well as bounds, on this growth curve for a given community. We discuss this in the following section. Actual growth data can then be compared with what might be, and judgments about performance can then be made.

In the fall of 1971, the system will be immersed more deeply and widely into the community by decentralizing the three-way telephone service into branch libraries of North Philadelphia. This creates a significant connection with the library community. It also raises another key problem amenable to operations research: Is there an optimal degree of decentralization? If so, what is it? Initial operational analyses of this general problem have been reported elsewhere [14–15].

To refer clients to agencies likely to help with emergency food, housing, and jobs—which account for most of the requests—I & R specialists seem still able to rely on memory. To enhance their memories, they are provided with a computer-generated directory. Initially, the present directory was prepared from a composite of thirty-five existing directories. It has multiple listings of about 2,800 records pertaining to social service agencies and their subprograms plus subject headings, all interfiled alphabetically by agency name and subject headings in about 3,000 pages of computer printout. A Thesaurus with cross-references is still under construction.[5]

The second key problem is designing this directory so that it will improve the performance of I & R specialists. They need the directory for problems concerning, in order of priority: employment, housing (needed new units and needed repairs), education, consumer and law, and social welfare (family, personal, and neighborhood difficulties). It must be understandable, easy to use, and above all, capable of providing selectivity to a growing data base of community resources, and of increasing sensitivity to individual clients' needs.

One feature of a directory that may give it the above qualities is "zoomability," a new concept to be intro-

duced in this paper. The problem this feature is meant to help solve has faced designers of catalogs and indexes for some time: how to permit a directory user who does not know the main entries appropriate to his query to locate an appropriate entry *quickly*.

It is only when the data base to which the directory has to orient its users becomes very large that the problem is acute and requires newer ideas and methods for solution. How can operations research contribute? In at least two ways. First and most important, its mathematical and scientific approach to problems helps clarify the basic ideas, leads to new concepts, and provides precise problem statements. It permits us to think analytically about the key problems. Second, it can actually supply new tools and methods to solve the problems. The next two sections deal with these two aspects.

ANALYSIS OF INFORMATION NETWORKS

Operations Research (O. R.) aims at providing a scientific basis for problem solving and decision making about the operations under a manager's jurisdiction. As such, the first contribution O. R. can make toward the creation of viable networks of I & R centers is to explicate, or clarify, the logical nature of the phenomena under study. This means primarily the creation of mathematical models which, even if they idealize and oversimplify, at least permit us to explore the logical boundaries of the existing conceptual framework. Concomitant with such modeling is the formulation of key problems and new ideas and concepts.

As a first instance of a mathematical model, consider a single I & R center such as the MCIC in North Philadelphia. Suppose its performance is to be

---

[5] Compare this with a book-form directory to community resources in Cleveland [16]. This consists of (1) a table of contents having nine main headings, an average of four subheads per main head (standard deviation of 3), and two sub-subheads per subhead (standard deviation of 3.3); (2) an index of about 1,100 terms; and (3) descriptions, including telephone numbers, for about 1,000 agencies.

described by the number of questions it receives per unit time, and how this number grows with time. This kind of data is available. In a crude sense, it can be used to evaluate performance, because satisfied clients would tend to use the system again or spread the word to others, causing the number of queries per unit time to increase up to the limits of its capacity.

The mathematical model described in Appendix A permits us to calculate such a growth curve with the help of a computer program. The basic assumptions, of which the growth curve is an implication, are that a user whose requests are serviced adequately will become a more frequent user; also, that as the number of queries serviced increases the probability of servicing a request adequately will increase until the number of requests per unit time is about 80 percent of capacity.[6] At that point, the probability of a satisfactory response begins to decrease due to congestion and overload effects.[7]

[6] In classical operations research [17, p. 199], it has been often assumed that very long times between requests are rare events (the probability of the time decreases as a negative exponential) with $1/a$ time units being the average lapse between requests; also that the time needed to answer requests is similarly distributed, with $1/b$ being the time. That is, when $b = 1$, it takes one time unit, say fifteen minutes on the average, to deal with a case. The fraction of time the server is busy is a/b, or a, since $b = 1$. As a increases, the time a client with a request can expect to wait for service to begin increases; the standard deviation of this waiting increases even faster. Even when the server is busy only 80 percent of the time, the client can expect to wait four time units with a variance of twenty-four (standard deviation of about 5). This increases to nine time units with a standard deviation of almost 10 if the server is busy 90 percent of the time. This may already be intolerably high, particularly the standard deviation.

[7] Of course, some questions recur, and a few common query types may account for the majority of cases. The center becomes very proficient

The reader who is not wholly adverse to mathematics should read Appendixes A–C. They contain the new work in this paper, and illustrate O. R. itself rather than talk about it.

The model permits us to explore the logical determinants of growth rate. The major one is the probability of a user becoming a more frequent user; this probability changes with time according to a law that can be partially controlled by the I & R Center's manager through the choice of a suitable directory and an appropriate advertising-educational strategy. The analysis of the model leads to the general conclusion that the daily case load can be made to increase up to a point by introducing a suitable improvement strategy in the design of the directory system. For example, if a query term occurs in one day's requests that is not in the directory system, it will be present after that day. One practical use of the computer program that computes the daily case load is to predict when the case load will begin to level off because of constraints on system capacity; if he wishes, the system manager can expand capacity to a new level and calculate the new case load growth curve this would imply. He can thus make planning decisions with sufficient lead time to carry them out.

As a second instance of a mathematical model, consider a network of "referential consultants."[8] Prior analysis [18] of one such model has suggested that a network can have greater utility than the smartest consultant standing alone. The conditions under which this is so, for a given value of

in servicing such common queries, and can thus stretch its capacity.

[8] We shall use this term interchangeably with "I & R specialist."

the model's parameter, is that the value of an acceptable answer be more than three times the penalty of an unacceptable answer. The model has the following features:

1. There are x "referential consultants," each of whom can field questions from a client or a colleague, responding to them either (a) directly, with some probability that his answer will satisfy the client, or (b) indirectly, by referring the question to a colleague likely to know more. Each referential consultant is characterized by three probabilities: (1) that he knows the answer to a randomly selected question; (2) that he will refer it to a particular colleague in a network when he does not know the answer; and that he will answer it when he does know the answer.

2. It is assumed that knowledge of whether any referential consultant answers a question to which he knows the answer does not change the probability of any other consultant answering the questions when he knows the answer.

3. The utility to the client of a satisfactory response is a certain number v, independent of the question and the response time. The client's disutility of a final unacceptable answer (not a referral) is c, in the same units as v, but negative.

4. A network of x consultants is specified by the three probabilities mentioned in point 1 (above) for each of them, where x can vary. The second of these probabilities is really an array of $x - 1$ probabilities—one for each colleague to whom it might refer; it is this which specifies the network structure. The performance of the network is evaluated by the net expected utility to a client.

For example, consider a net of five ($x = 5$) consultants, R_1, R_2, R_3, R_4, and R_5. The first is smartest and can adequately answer 80 percent of the questions coming his way. The other four can only answer directly 3 percent of the questions addressed to them. The probability of nonreferral (or answering) when a consultant knows the answer was taken to be .9, and the probability of nonreferral (answering) when he does not know was taken to be .1.

If R_1 stands alone, he will respond adequately with probability $(.9)(.8) = .72$. But he will respond inadequately with probability $(.1)(.2) = .02$. He will provide a service with an expected net utility of $.72v - .02c$ units. The client gets no response (utility 0) with probability .26.

Now, suppose that R_1 does not stand alone, but is the first recipient of each request. If he does not answer he refers the question to R_2, who refers it (if need be) to R_3, who passes to R_4, who passes to R_5. But R_5, if need be, refers it back to R_4. The probability that R_1 will refer is the probability that he knows and does not answer, $(.1)(.8)$, plus the probability that he does not know and cannot answer, $(.9)(.2)$ or $.08 + .18 = .26$. There is then a small probability that R_2 can answer adequately, when R_1 could not—$(.26) \times (.9)(.03)$. The probability of the client receiving an adequate response from either R_1 or R_2 is thus $.72 + (.26)(.027)$. In a similar way, we can calculate the probability that a client receives an adequate response from R_1, R_2, R_3, R_4, or R_5. We then find that the net utility of the network to the client is $.743v - .104c$, compared with $.720v - .020c$ for R_1 by himself. The network's net utility exceeds that of

R_1 alone when $.023v - .84c > 0$, that is, when $v/c > 3$. A situation where a wrong answer causes little damage and a correct answer helps a great deal—such as a contest, solving a riddle for a prize, or betting on a nonchance event with great odds—meets this condition. There, five heads (even one genius supported by four knuckleheads) are better than one head (the genius).

As a third instance of a mathematical model, not developed as extensively as the two above, we analyze a directory to a data base giving information about poisons. Imagine the data base as a table with D lines. In this case, the data base itself is a directory to antidotes. The lines are alphabetically ordered by the name of a poison. Each line also includes an output naming the best antidote. Because the terms used to describe the properties of poisons and their effects on people vary greatly from one reporter to another (and even from one situation to another for the same reporter), and also because D is very large, such a poison control directory has much in common with a directory to the social services of a community, and with many other directories as well. It is a good vehicle for exposition and analysis.

Let us imagine, further, that each of the D entries can either directly match a term chosen by the client or his referential consultant, or be specified by a conjunction of n terms. For example, an entry might be "mercury," or equivalently, "silvery, liquid, and globular" with $n = 3$. Moreover, each of the n property-designating terms are in a binary tree representing a classification hierarchy (see fig. 1). Each tree has λ levels. This is exemplified with $\lambda = 4$.

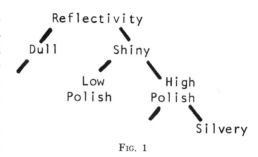

FIG. 1

The directory user can try to match his terms either with any of the D terms in the directory or any of the $n \times (1 + 2 + 4 + \ldots + 2^{\lambda-1})$ terms at any of the n associated trees. Each term he picks has thus only $D + nx (2^\lambda - 1)$ chances out of Q possible terms he might use to match a term associated with the directory. He can fail to accomplish the purpose that the directory is to help him attain (e.g., find an antidote in time to save a victim of poisoning) in three ways: (1) none of his query terms match anything in or associated with the directory—either because the thesaurus is not as yet rich enough to represent all that is known about poisons or its users' language or because not all the poisons are as yet known; (2) his query terms match but identify the poisons only to within one of a set, and he makes an unfortunate choice (by chance) within that set;[9] and (3) his query terms pinpoint the poison precisely, but too late.[10]

[9] Vagueness in a query incurs risk of getting the wrong antidote, while use of vocabulary foreign to the directory system incurs the risk of no response at all.

[10] We do not dwell on other possible causes of failure: that the poison may still be unknown, or be known and have no known antidote; that both are known but not yet with reliable certainty; or that the news has not yet been incorporated in the directory. Nor do we stress that the utility of a response may decrease discontinuously at a certain point for poisons—a

If the directory with its associated aids contained a complete description of each poison, its users could, by reading the entire directory from start to finish, recognize the poison he was concerned with. He could not perhaps, on his own, have asked his client (or himself) all the questions, the answers to which would have led *directly* to the poison in question. Complete perusal of the directory is too time-consuming and inconvenient in an essential way. Expecting each user to know all the appropriate terms that could be main entries is too unrealistic. Designing a directory structure which steers a middle course is a key problem [19].

Through cross-references [20–22], a user could be led from terms he has thought of to terms he has not, which might help. This, too, can be time-consuming without enhancing the probability of success sufficiently, although it is better than a straight coordinate index without such a thesaurus. A hierarchical thesaurus such as that shown in figure 1 might help even more, but it could be time-wasting if everyone had to use it—even the user who knows the precise terms at the bottom of the tree. A decision table [23] is a powerful tool (from O. R.) that could be used to implement such a thesaurus. However, it would be limited to one tree, and inhibit jumping laterally from one tree to another.

What might help most is a semantic zoom lens,[11] which permits a user to

choose a term at a high level in the hierarchical classification scheme associated with the directory, and then to see in one glance, with overall perspective, the entire range of terms subsumed by that term, although not in full detail. This zoom lens should be controllable by him, allowing him to blow up into full detail any part of the directory subsumed by the generic term, and then perhaps go back to a high-altitude perspective, pick another generic term, etc. He could thus begin by seeing in one glance the gross structure of the entire tree, including the bottom nodes, pick a goal, and then examine in detail a node and the ones below it. In this manner, he could follow a path and check whether it was leading toward the goal. He could pick subgoals and move in subpaths. This appears to give the required speed; at the same time, it affords fuller use of the directory system to pinpoint the poison more precisely [19].

Appendixes B and C show how such directories can be improved with experience, and how a good directory can improve the performance of an I & R center. Out of such analyses, further insights into the basic limitations of conventionally organized directories, such as the "Yellow Pages" or a library catalog, are possible. At the same time, ideas such as the above can be developed to overcome these limitations. The designer of an I & R center can control these "learning" features of his growing directory system [26].

Although we have not delved into it in mathematical detail, we can sketch the general lines of thought that should go into completing this analysis of directories. The next step is to derive an

___

nature-imposed deadline—which may be restricted to such emergency cases as would reach a poison control center. Quite generally, however, the utility of a response decreases as the response time gets large, even in a library whose patrons aim to utilize their leisure.

[11] An aspect of this idea was anticipated in Doyle's "Semantic Road Maps" [24], and de-

veloped further by Rolling in the *EURATOM Thesaurus* [25].

expression for the average utility of a specified directory. This will depend on the utility of a "hit" (e.g., of being able to pinpoint the correct poison and its antidote exactly, and very rapidly). In situations where the degree of accuracy and precision in such pinpointing can be traded off against time, both the average time and average disutility of two types of errors must be considered. The first type is accepting a certain substance as the cause of a poisoning when it was not; the second is failing to accept a substance as causative when it was.

The utility will also depend on the size of the data base to which the directory points. If we plot the average utility against the size of the data base, we will get a variety of curves that depend on the structure of the directory system. For a straight coordinate index, the utility should decrease as data base increases: it takes longer and longer to pinpoint an item as there are more items to select from; if it must be done quickly, selectivity becomes less and less fine. For a directory system in which the thesauri associated with the directory have variable zoomability, the expected utility per query can be made to increase as the size of the data base grows.

The next step is to plot operating cost against data base size. This has three components: (1) cost of updating, (2) cost of searching, and (3) cost of storage. Initial costs could be distributed over operating costs for the life of the system.

We then seek a directory system structure for which the average utility per query grows with increasing data base size more rapidly than does cost. We expect a subsequent analysis to show that a directory system with variable zoomability has this property.

To connect this with our central theme of directories for network analysis, note that a directory which is good in the above sense causes $p(t)$, the probability of the user of an I & R center to become a more frequent user, to be higher. Because the time it takes to match the telephone query received by a referential consultant or I & R specialist with what he can find in his index to sources is shorter if a better directory is used, the probability of a query being adequately serviced is higher. If other factors are equal, this will generate more use of the system and make a network more effective. In the next section we describe a tool for exploring the costs as well.

NEW TOOLS AND METHODS

Operations Research also provides techniques useful in solving some of the problems arising in the analysis and design of cost-effective information nets. Usually these are optimization techniques to help managers most effectively deploy scarce resources. The appendixes and cited references show the use of calculus, probability theory, matrix algebra, and graph theory—all of which are branches of mathematics widely used in O. R. The main tool to be illustrated here is a new computer program that helps analyze and design directories for the use of a network of referential consultants.

This program was first described in a prior work [27]. When given an input question and the referential to whom this question is first given, its output is: (1) the cost of providing the answer, and (2) the chain of consultants and the document used to provide the answer.

This program takes into account the use of directories which each referential consultant is assumed to use. It begins by specifying four tables that can be varied for different runs. In all four tables, each row corresponds to a referential consultant. Each column corresponds to a request the client might make. The first row of the first table has as an entry for each request a set of numbers that represent either other referential consultants or documents, each of which the consultant R_1 can *rely* upon to supply an acceptable answer. This represents a directory to reliable sources of information and referral. The second row of the first table is a corresponding directory for referential consultant R_2. The entire table 1 summarizes all the directories for each question; the entries represent documents or colleagues that each of the consultants in the network can *rely* upon as sources for question answering or referral.

The second table contains directories, one for each consultant, to *colleagues* to whom the consultant can refer questions because he thinks they are more likely than he to answer or refer the question satisfactorily. It contains entries only for cases where table 1 has no entry. The third table gives the costs to the user of getting an answer to a specified question from a source listed in the first table. The fourth table gives the costs of transferring a question to a colleague specified in the second table.

For example, suppose that the third column corresponds to the question. Where can I get food stamps? Con-

sider the following entries in row 1 (for consultant R_1) and column 3:

Table 1.—R_2, R_4, D_3, D_8 (the cell in row 1, column 3 has these four identifiers). This means that R_1 can *rely* on getting an acceptable answer by either asking colleague R_2, colleague R_4 or looking it up in documents D_3 or D_8.

Table 2.—0 (the cell in row 1, column 3 has only a 0). This means that since he can *rely* on any of four sources (all supplementary to his memory) to get the needed telephone number, there are *no* other colleagues to whom he would transfer the entire request. If the entry in table 1 (row 1, column 3) had been 0, meaning that R_1 has *no reliable* source to use for the request, then the cell (row 1, column 3) in table 2 might have been R_3, R_5, This means that he would consider both colleagues R_3 and R_5 better qualified to handle this request than he does himself.

Table 3.—1, 1, 2, 3 (the cell in row 1, column 3 has these four numbers). This means that it costs R_1 one unit to consult either colleague R_2 or R_4, that it costs him two units to consult source D_3, and three units to consult D_8.

Table 4.—If the entry in table 2 is 0, the entry in this table is 0; if he does not transfer the request, there is no corresponding cost. Otherwise, the cost could be one unit—the same as consulting a colleague.

With these four tables, given any values assigned and stored prior to running the program, various runs can now be made. The input to any single run is a request—corresponding to one of the columns—and a referential consultant to whom that request is first directed—corresponding to one of the rows. The program then tries all the choices for responding to the request, and searches for the trail of lowest cost. For that trail, it then prints out the various referential consultants who are passed the request, the sources they consulted and in what order, and the cost. This is repeated for all possible requests, if desired, and an average cost is computed. Then the four input tables are varied, corresponding to different networks and/or different directories for each referential consultant. The least cost averaged over all requests can then be compared for different directories and networks.

This program can be made available to anyone wishing to explore the cost-effectiveness of various directory structures and network configurations. Very few of these explorations have as yet been made. Many refinements in this program have been made and many more can easily be incorporated. The kind of insight about the structure of directories that can be obtained with the help of this program is illustrated in my paper, "Switching Centers for Inquiry Referral" [27].

The program described here resembles a class of computer uses called simulation. There are quite a number of powerful, high-level computer programming languages, [28; 29, p. 117] that simplify such computer uses, however, we used FORTRAN rather than such a specialized language, because our problem is quite simple, and FORTRAN costs less. In our program, the fate of each input query is traced, and the behavior of referential consultants is simulated. An extension or elaboration of this program might simulate the behavior of the users as well. In the first place, the program described in this section could be specialized to include *hierarchies* of referential consultants, each associated with a hierarchically structured directory similar to that discussed at the end of the last section. In this scheme, some referential consultants would be generalists and some specialists, with appropriate referral strategies and directories assigned to each. Some R's would have larger and more comprehensive responsibilities and resources and would therefore stand higher in the hierarchy. The advantages and limitations of hierarchies are discussed in [5]. This program would give us a tool for determining an optimum degree of hierarchization when that exists.

Second, the client-users of the system can be characterized by variables representing their possible choices which are listed at the end of Appendix A. Built into the program are assumptions about how a choice like approaching or not approaching R_1 with inquiry q, depends on, say, advertising; the latter might be quantified by the quintuple $(x_1, x_2, x_3, x_4, x_5)$, where x_i is the amount of money spent on the use of newspapers $(i = 1)$, television $(i = 2)$, mailing of brochures $(i = 3)$, door-to-door personal contact $(i = 4)$, automatic telephone calling $(i = 5)$.

Different clients would respond to a given mix $(x_1, \ldots, x_5)$ in different ways, depending on their backgrounds (educational, ethnic), socioeconomic status, etc. A computer program called MEDIA-MIX[12] uses such demographic data about a community to simulate how a sample of individuals would react to a media mix. It then computes

[12] Developed by and obtained from Simulmatics, Inc., 16 East 41st Street, New York, New York 10017.

a mix, $(x_1, \ldots, x_5)$, which gives an advertiser the greatest effect or reach for the least cost. The success of the MEDIA-MIX programs in the advertising industry and in analyzing political behavior suggests that it may be equally fruitful in solving some of the key problems in analyzing and designing information systems.

Of particular interest might be a new advertising-educational device unique to I & R centers, corresponding to the fifth possibility in the above mentioned mix. It appears that more than half of the I & R needs in certain communities pertain to only a few major concerns (e.g., emergency food, housing). Moreover, I & R specialists seem able to provide an adequate response to most of these inquiries with only a few telephone numbers of agencies that meet such needs. If a large fraction of the people who have not used the I & R center also have such needs, then an effective campaign might be to call systematically each of these people, volunteer to them a pre-recorded response to these latent requests, inform them that the I & R center exists and invites inquiries on almost *any* other topic. The names could be drawn from a telephone directory using a map. The job of calling can be automated and made cost-effective with the telephone company's automatic calling system. Alternative 3 might be even more cost-effective by mailing a suitable flyer to all occupants of an area. Alternative 2 would probably be most effective but also very costly.

CONCLUSIONS

Operations research (or at least an applied mathematician presenting a paper at a conference entitled "Opera-

tions Research: Implications for Libraries") can help solve at least two real problems faced by an innovator-manager of an information and referral center such as the MCIC in North Philadelphia. It contributes the following to the analysis and design of directories: logical structuring, new concepts like "zoomability," and new tools like the computer program for tracing the path and cost of a request through a network of referential consultants. To the problem of getting the community to realize and utilize the services of an I & R center network, it also contributes a formulation of the key problem: how to specify and create conditions ensuring the viable growth of a cost-effective service. It leads, indirectly, to ideas for solving this problem, such as the use of an automatic telephone calling system or mailings of flyers to all occupants of an area to acquaint a large selection of potential clients with answers to the few questions accounting for 80 percent of cases now handled; at the same time that such clients are given a sample of the center's service, they are informed of the center's existence and the very broad scope of questions it is equipped to field. Operations research contributes, above all, analytical insights into the logical nature of the problem and helps explore the boundaries of logically possible solutions.

Such operations analyses are necessary, but not sufficient, for realizing the valuable potential of networks of I & R centers in a cost-effective way and with a rational basis. Operations Research *contributes* to real problem solving; it cannot do the entire job alone. To create conditions that encourage clients to use a system requires vigorous, dedicated, enthusiastic, competent full-time entrepreneurial commitment; ample resources in money, space, and people; absence of too many adverse circumstances, some of which always occur; good salesmanship, public relations, image building and advertising; and, of course, a high quality service. To create a good directory takes more than good design; it also requires rapport with and involvement of its users in its development. All these are some of the necessary and sufficient conditions for maximizing cost-effectiveness of a net of I & R centers. To enable operations research to realize its full potential contribution, it is also necessary to have suitably trained "popularizers" who can interpret, explain, and apply the technical accomplishments for those responsible for operations.

But realizing the potential of operations research has merely begun. For analytically oriented researchers in the library and information sciences, these beginnings open up a vast, and in my opinion, potentially very fruitful and exciting area of investigation. There is, for example, a great deal of important work to be done in solving the more general systems of equations given at the end of Appendix A. On the analytic side, newer mathematical techniques of solving partial differential equations like the diffusion equations with nonconstant coefficients can give greater analytical insight into how the amount of use of an information net grows. On the numerical side, there are many opportunities for solving very realistic models with the help of computers.

For more experimentally and empirically oriented researchers in the library and information sciences, there is a great need and challenge to investigate the behavior of the user-clients for the services of I & R networks. Under what conditions does a user with a need decide to pose a question? How does he select the source to which he addresses his request? With what expectations? What rules govern the structure of his request: its phraseology and its relation to this need; what it says, when, and to whom; how it is modified by responses to prior questions? The same investigation applies also to the I & R specialists and others who mediate between would-be recipients of, say, social services at one end and those who dispense these services at the other.

Designing a good directory requires such hard data about human factors as limits on (and optimal match with) the capacities of directory users for visual perception, cognitive memory and processing, and affective and aesthetic evaluation. Different users should get different directories, but how should the assignment be made? A generalist referential consultant should have a very comprehensive directory with variable "zoomability." A more specialized referential consultant should have a directory covering a narrower topic in greater depth, but coupled into the directory of his generalist colleague. The ultimate client-user, too, should have a summary directory, perhaps a one-page overview that is part of the brochure describing the system to him, with options for requesting and getting more detailed directories for a closeup view of some topic.

In a few years, if scientific approaches to these problems are pressed at a vigorous pace, there should be enough accomplishment to   decrease significantly the entrepreneurial risk of setting up new I & R centers and networks. These risks can never be completely eliminated. It is important that sufficiently bold and far-sighted innovators, like Dr. J. Ball, proceed right now, to create viable enterprises. These managers of innovations should keep up with the advances in O. R. that can be applied to their art. At least, they should establish contact with people who can mediate between those responsible for these advances and themselves. The systems they develop will be the most valuable sources of experience, data, problems, guidance for analysis and new ideas, as well as possible testing grounds for the contributions from operations research.

For somewhat similar reasons, managers of traditional I & R centers or networks would benefit from the intellectual currents resulting from O. R. in their area. Many good choices (decisions) have been made without a sound scientific basis. Whether it was good "business sense" emerging from practical experience, an innate talent, ESP, or just plain luck, the demands on these capabilities become much greater as the tasks requiring decisions become more complex and as the number of such tasks increases. There is, moreover, a shortage of sufficiently experienced and competent middle management personnel. The use of information technology, guided by O. R., can help face this shortage by amplifying the capacity of existing middle managers. So can people who can stimulate fruitful contacts among middle managers to share experiences; operations researchers and their interpreters are such people. However, research on nets of I & R centers is so recent that there cannot yet be many results with a direct impact on the needs of managers of established enterprises in this field. It is, however, important that these managers appreciate and support O. R. for future results. The process of investigation often leads to useful contacts that the investigator can make with managers; for example, the preparation of this paper led to my learning about Dr. Ball, who is willing to share his knowledge of such promising innovations as the three-way telephone with other managers of I & R centers.

Finally, educators and students in the information sciences should be oriented toward, and be given the options of learning O. R. in their fields. In particular, it is important to educate enough highly creative people who can add to the basic concepts and methods; at the same time we must educate a larger number of creative people who can use this knowledge to solve real problems. For both it is important to provide good grounding in the fundamentals of mathematical thinking and scientific method. It is equally important that this be regarded as education rather than training, and that it be blended with and dominated by the humanistic orientation that has characterized some of the best thought in the library sciences.

APPENDIX A

MODEL FOR GROWTH IN USAGE OF AN I & R CENTER

One way to measure success of a service is to look for growth in the number of frequent users. Consider the following basic variables to be used for stating some plausible assumptions governing the growth of such a service center and for deriving their implications:

t = the number of days after the center became operational (real number).

f = an average frequency of using the system; a user is said to be in state f, if, were he to use the system forever and with no change, he would use it f times per day or once every $1/f$ days on the average; we take f to lie between 0 and 1 inclusive. Being in state $f = 0$ is to be a nonuser; being in state $f = 1$ is to use it daily. (This can be treated as a real number, also.)

M = the size of the population from which users are drawn. This is assumed to be fixed.

$N(t,f)$ = the number of people in state f on the tth day. This is a random variable, but for simplicity we will deal only with the average, $EN(t,f)$.

$p(t)$ = the conditional probability of a randomly chosen user being in state f on day t, given that he was in state $f - \Delta f$ on day $t - \Delta t$. Here Δf and Δt are arbitrary fractions (of days), taken to be .001 and 1 in the numerical calculations to follow. It is also assumed that this is a Markov process, with $p(t)$ independent of f.

$r(t)$ = the conditional probability of being in state f on day t, given state f also on day $t - \Delta t$.

$q(t) = 1 - p(t) - r(t)$.

The expected number of people in state f on day $t + \Delta t$ thus depends only on the expected number of people in states $f - \Delta f$ and $f + \Delta f$ on day t. The element $EN(t + \Delta t, f) - EN(t,f)$ increases due to in-migration from states $f - \Delta f$, an event of probability $p(t)$, and from state $f + \Delta f$, an event of probability $q(t)$. But it also decreases by out-migration from state f to state $f + \Delta f$, with probability $p(t)$, and to $f - \Delta t$, with probability $q(t)$. The change is 0 with probability $r(t)$. Thus,

$$EN(t + \Delta t, f) = EN(t, f)$$
$$+ p(t)[EN(t, f - \Delta f) - EN(t, f)]$$
$$+ q(t)[EN(t, f + \Delta f) - EN(t, f)]. \quad (1)$$

If $r(t) = 0$, the $p(t)$ (or p for short) = $1 - q$ and

$$EN(t + \Delta t, f) = pEN(t, f - \Delta f)$$
$$+ qEN(t, f + \Delta f). \quad (2)$$

Initially, at $t = 0$, we suppose that

$$N(0, f) = \begin{cases} M, & \text{if} \quad f = 0 \\ 0, & \text{if} \quad f > 0. \end{cases} \quad (3)$$

We suppose next that $p(t)$ is specified for all t and proceed to calculate $EN(t,f)$ numerically, according to the above formulas, plus the conditions

$$\sum_f N(t, f) = M, \quad (4)$$

for all t.

Equations (2)–(4) have been solved with the help of a FORTRAN computer program. In the first model for which this program was run, $p(t)$, the probability of a user becoming a more frequent user, was chosen somewhat arbitrarily, to start the series of investigations, as follows:

$$p(t) = \begin{cases} K \sum_{\tau=0}^{t-1} \dfrac{R(\tau)}{OV}[1 - p(\tau)] & \text{if} \quad R(t) \leqslant OV \\[2em] \dfrac{OV}{R(\tau)} \cdot K \sum_{\tau=0}^{t-1} \dfrac{R(\tau)}{OV}[1 - p(\tau)] & \text{if} \quad R(t) > OV. \end{cases}$$

Here, $R(\tau)$ is the daily case load on day τ. It is

$$\sum_f fN(\tau, f),$$

where $fN(\tau,f)$ is the total number or requests coming from frequency class f on day τ. All incoming requests are serviced, provided the daily case load is less than the overload point OV. When $R(t)$ exceeds OV cases/day, the probability of a user becoming a more frequent user decreases, even though it may have reached 1 when $R(t) = OV$. Up to $R(t) = OV$, $p(t)$ increases steadily in proportion to the expected number of cases which offer opportunities for system improvement,

$$\sum_\tau R(\tau)[1 - p(\tau)].$$

The "learning factor" K can be interpreted as the number of cases on which improvement is based, divided by the total number of cases on which improvement could be based.

$$+ q \frac{EN(t, f + \Delta f) - EN(t, f)}{\Delta f} \Big].$$

If we take the limit of both sides as $\Delta t \to 0$ and $\Delta f \to 0$, then

$$\frac{\partial EN}{\partial t} = \frac{df}{dt}\left(q \frac{\partial EN}{\partial f} - p \frac{\partial EN}{\partial f}\right). \quad (5)$$

If, moreover $p = q$, then

$$\frac{\partial EN}{\partial t} = \frac{df}{dt} \cdot p \frac{\partial^2 EN}{\partial f^2}. \quad (6)$$

This is the diffusion equation, analogous to the conduction of heat or spread of solute, with $(df/dt)p$ the rate of diffusion over frequency states. Since this is a function of t, and since separation of variables—that is, assuming that $EN(t,f) = EN_1(t) EN_2(f)$ is quite unrealistic—this partial differential equation is quite difficult to solve analytically.

In a more general model, which is not constrained by the restriction that a user can migrate only to or from a neighboring

TABLE A1
VALUES ON USAGE PRINTED OUT BY COMPUTER

	DAY NUMBER (t)						
	100	200	500	1,000	2,000	3,000	4,000
Daily case load, $R(t)$ ...	0.28	0.78	23.2	4,065	4,091	4,095	4,096
Total no. active users ...	276	782	20,824	193,453	191,237	190,903	190,793

NOTE.—In the case of this printout, $M = 200,000$, $OV = 2,000$, $p(0) = .0005$, $p(1) = .000505$, and $K = .1051$.

Table A1 shows an example of the values on usage printed out by the computer. Note the rapid increase in total number of users up to a day between the 500th and the 1,000th at which the overload point is reached. Thereafter, users begin to drop out.

If we divide both sides of equation (1) by Δt and multiply the numerator and denominator on the right-hand side by Δf, we get:

$$\frac{EN(t + \Delta t, f) - EN(t, f)}{\Delta t} = \frac{\Delta f}{\Delta t} \cdot$$

$$\left[p \frac{EN(t, f) - EN(t, f - \Delta f)}{\Delta f} \right.$$

frequency state, we define $P(\chi|\phi;t)$: the conditional probability that a randomly chosen user is in state χ at time $t + \Delta t$ given that he was in state ϕ at time t. This replaces $p(t)$. We now have, in place of equation (1), the following:

$$EN(t + \Delta t, f) = EN(t, f)$$

$$+ \sum_{\substack{\phi \\ \phi \neq f}} p(f/\phi; t) EN(t, \phi)$$

$$- \sum_{\substack{\chi \\ \chi \neq f}} p(\chi/f; t) EN(t, \chi). \quad (1')$$

Even more generally, if we were interested in the entire distribution of $N(t,f)$ rather than merely its mean, we could define p_k

$(t,f) = \mathrm{Prob}[N(t,f) = k]$, $k = 0, 1, \ldots,$ and many other interesting analyses could *M* and write: be performed.

$$p_k(t + \Delta t, f) = \sum_{a=0}^{M} p_a(t, f) \cdot \sum_{\substack{l \\ a+l=k}} \sum_{\phi} p(f/\phi; t) p_l(t, \phi) \cdot \sum_{\substack{l \\ a-l=k}} \sum_{\chi} p(\chi/f; t) p_l(t, \chi),$$

$$(1'')$$

$k = 0, \ldots, M$. This is a convolution. It can be transformed into a system of $M + 1$ simultaneous linear equations by taking Fourier transforms of $p_k(t,f)$. This system can be solved with the help of matrix algebra and $p_k(t,f)$ can then be obtained by applying inverse Fourier transforms.

In view of this considerable computational effort, it may be desirable to simulate the behavior of users in terms of a few random variables like:

$$U_i(t) = \begin{cases} 1 \text{ if user i uses the system} \\ \quad \text{at time } t, \\ 0 \text{ if not;} \end{cases}$$

$S_i(t) = 1$ if user *i*'s query at time *t* was handled satisfactorily, 0 if not, given that he posed a query; $Q_i(t) = 1$ if he posed a query at *t*, 0 if not; $C_{ij}(t)$ if *i* heard good things about the system from source *j* at *t*, 0 if not; etc. This "Monte-Carlo" procedure could then be used to print out $p_k(t,f)$,

Here *i* denotes the *i*th of *M* users. Instead of operating a computer program for each of the *M* simulated users, this is done only for a sample of *M'* users, where $M' << M$. Values of sociometric variables like employment, status, state of health, housing, educational level, marital status, sex, etc., are entered for each user so that for all *M'* of them, the statistics characterizing a community is represented. Also entered into the computer is an assumed probabilistic relationship between $U_i(t)$, $S_i(t)$, $Q_i(t)$, C_{ij}, and the values of these variables. The computer then assigns values to $U_i(t)$, etc., using a random-number generator biased according to the assumed relations and using the stored sociometric data.

Among other uses, comparing the average number of queries per day,

$$M' \sum_f f p(t, f),$$

with data can help test the validity of the assumed relations.

APPENDIX B

MODELS FOR IMPROVEMENT OF AN I & R CENTER

In the model of Appendix A, the function $p(t)$ was assumed to be given. We now derive it from various more or less plausible assumptions about how the system learns from failure and success.

In general, the probability of a user moving from a certain frequency-of-use state to one where he uses the system more frequently is a function of three probabilities: (1) he is aware of an as yet unmet need; (2) he knows about the system, through advertisement, word of mouth from others, or prior use and intends to use it; and (3) it is likely to meet his need and he believes this.

To make the problems mathematically tractable, let us focus only on the third probability and interpret $p(t)$ to be the probability of success for a randomly chosen request. To fix ideas, consider a directory to the antidotes of D out of Q possible poisons, with the client presumed to know the name of a poison which may match one of the D entries. The probability of success is then D/Q and of failure $(Q-D)/Q$. Suppose, however, the possibility of learning from failure: if the client specifies at time t a poison not among the D listed at that time, then this poison will appear in the list at time $t + \Delta t$ together with its antidote. Thus D depends on t and is a random variable. Let ED be the mean number of listed entries at time t and ED' the number at $t + \Delta t$.

If, during time interval $(t, t + \Delta t)$ there are exactly k queries about poisons not among the D poisons in the list at time t, each of which leads to an added entry in the directory, then $D' = ED + k$. On the average, $ED' = ED + Ek$, where E is the expectation operator. The probability that k entries are added is determined from $1 - p$, the probability that a single query is not one of the ED and R, the number of queries received in time interval $(t, t +$ $\Delta t)$, all assumed to be statistically independent. The probability of k entries being added is

$$\binom{R}{k}(1-p)^k \, p^{R-k}$$

and the average number Ek is $R(1 - p)$. This is multiplied by the "learning factor" used in Appendix A, with $R(t)$ as defined there also.

We thus have:

$$ED' = ED + KR(1 - p), \qquad (7)$$

with

$$p = p(t) = \frac{ED(t)}{Q}. \qquad (8)$$

A slightly more sophisticated model admits learning from success as well. Two new variables are needed: $k(t) = $ the average number of entries specified by a randomly chosen request, due to imprecision in the request, provided the request matches an entry in the directory at all; and $p_2(t) = $ the conditional probability that a request names the correct poison (and antidote) given that it hit the directory at all; $p_1(t) = p(t) = $ probability of matching the directory at all.

Now $p_1 p_2$ is the probability of success. As before, there is learning from failure—an event of probability p_1. We therefore have direct analogs of equations (7) and (8) in:

$$ED' = p_1 ED + (1 - p_1)(ED + KR)$$
$$= ED + KR(1 - p_1) \quad (9)$$

and

$$p_1' = (q_1 (ED + KR) + p_1 ED)/Q,$$
$$q_1 = 1 - p_1. \qquad (10)$$

But there is also learning from success. If the correct poison is hit upon, then k is reduced by $(k-1)/D$ on the average: the particular group of k poisons which the query hit is replaced by 1, but there were D groups of k (on the average) poisons hit by a query. Thus:

$$p_2 = \frac{1}{k}; \qquad (11)$$

$$k' = \left(k - \frac{KR}{ED}\right)(1 - p_2)\, p_1$$

$$+ \left(k - \frac{k-1}{ED}\, KR\right) p_2 p_1$$

$$+ k(1 - p_1). \qquad (12)$$

Computer programs to solve the systems of equations specified by these more sophisticated formulas in addition to that described in Appendix A have been written, but have only just begun to yield results. This FORTRAN program can be used at a teletypewriter terminal of a time-sharing system. It requires initial input values for M, the total population of the community served by an I & R center; Q, the set of all possible query terms any of these citizens might enter; D, the initial size of the directory; k, the initial number of terms in the directory to which a query term points; OV, the maximum tolerable daily case load; and K, the learning factor. It produces the following output in response to the on-line input t (day number): the total number of users to date; the case load that day; the probability of a directory hit; the probability of success, given a hit; the probabilities of success and failure; the current average values of k and of D. It can also plot the distribution of users over the 1,000 frequency classes in any run.

So far, the program has been run for the values shown in table B1.

Describing the outputs in detail requires considerable space and will be done in a separate future publication. Some general summary observations can be reported. In case 5 of table B1, the daily case load grows very slowly, and it is not quite one question per day by day 100. On day 5, all of the users are in the first six frequency classes; by day 25, they spread over the first twenty-two and by day 300, when the case load is 7.7 questions per day, it has a symmetric spread over classes 0–145. This distribution will continue to move up until the daily case load reaches fifty and then it will spread even more. In case 3, by contrast, the daily case load grows quite rapidly, reaching the overload point, 250 per day, shortly after day 500. Even at day 1,000, the distribution of users over frequency classes is still skewed, mostly over the first nine classes. Case (4) falls between (3) and (5)—the daily case load is increasing slowly.

This entire idea of a growing thesaurus, which was launched in 1965 [29], if analyzed as a scientific problem, can avoid the controversy about authority structures. The kind of directories needed in I & R centers have a rapidly changing data base of a different quality than that dealt with by librarians. The cataloging standards evolved in the library profession are not functional here and create unnecessary delay and cost. Some organizational system, however, is needed.

This operating program invites a number of extensions and improvements, as well as numerous explorations. For one thing, M

TABLE B1

INPUT VALUES THUS FAR RUN FOR THE FORTRAN PROGRAM

	M	Q	$D(O)$	$k(O)$	OV	K
1	200,000	20,000	200	15	2,000	.01
2	200,000	2,000	1,000	10	20,000	.01
3	200,000	2,000	1,000	10	250	.50
4	200,000	100,000	10,000	3	250	.50
5	100	200	199	2	50	.50

does not remain fixed; neither does OV. Furthermore, users in high-frequency states are less likely to become even more frequent users than would users in lower frequency states, because most of their needs will already have been met. Above all, the refinements suggested at the end of Appendix A and in Appendix C should be incorporated, and the program should be used in conjunction with the two programs for network and directory analysis described in the body of the paper.

These programs can be made available to anyone interested in using or adding to them by writing to me or to A. Breveleri at the University of Michigan, Mental Health Research Institute, Ann Arbor, Michigan 48104.

A MODEL FOR CALCULATING THE ZOOMABILITY OF A DIRECTORY

In Appendix B, failure occurred in two ways: (1) the query term used by the client $+$ I & R specialist was not among the D main entries of the directory, and (2) the directory was hit by the query, but any one of k terms in the directory could correspond to the query, with $k-1$ being erroneous and one right. We now consider a third kind of failure: (3) the correct one of k terms in the directory is hit, but too late; it took more comparisons between directory entries and query terms than are acceptable.

Still using a directory for poison control as a vehicle, note that a client generally will not know the precise chemical name of a poison for which he needs an antidote. Instead, he engages in a conversation with the I & R specialist and supplies him with descriptive terms about the substance and the symptoms, either in response to the specialist's question or on his own. Let us now visualize the directory. Instead of a table with one column of D main entries, a matrix of D entries, with R rows and K columns, $R \times K = D$, in this directory each row corresponds to a precisely named property of a substance (i.e., to a class of substances with that property), and each column to a unique sign or symptom (i.e., to a class of poisons capable of producing that set of signs or symptoms).

Let us further view the R substances as the endpoints of a tree corresponding to a particular way (one of many that are possible) of classifying the properties of substances. Suppose, for example, that a first-level breakdown is by visual properties —solid, liquid, gas, or other; a second-level breakdown for solid might be: powder, chunky, etc. A particular substance might thus be identified as a fine powder, with a smooth, flaky texture. Specifying only that it is solid might cover $k = 100$ possible rows (i.e., substances). Specifying symptoms like nausea, etc. would reduce it further to $k = 50$ possible entries (poisons $+$ antidotes) in the table.

The I & R specialist could, by playing the game of "twenty questions," tease out of the client such data as would pinpoint the set of possible substances quite rapidly. He could ask yes-no questions, such as Was it solid or not? Was it powdery or not? He does this by moving up or down along a particular tree, such as a state-of-matter tree. If the client specifies at the outset that the substance was powdery, or if the interviewer (I & R specialist) has reason to suspect it was powdery, then he should be able to enter the directory at a point near the bottom of the state-of-matter tree. Otherwise, he might begin his twenty-question sequence near the top.

We have illustrated a directory with entries corresponding to the bottom nodes of just two trees. In general, there will be many; some of these trees may be used in parallel, others must be consulted in one or more specified sequences. We shall assume only serial processing, with all questions and answers in a linear sequence, so that all separate trees are used in conjunction in some specified order. Thus, the state-of-matter tree might be used first; then the color tree; then a taste-tree, then a smell-tree; then a tactile tree; then the various sign-symptom trees in conjunction. The final result is a coordinate entry in the directory, such as powdery, white, sour, acrid, cold to touch, nausea, headache, etc.

We will focus in this discussion on only one tree. Suppose it has two branches at each node and $\lambda + 1$ levels—the single node at the top being level λ and the bottom level 0. There are 2^λ nodes at level 0. The questioner climbs down the tree by asking yes-no questions, and selecting one of the two branches depending on the answer. Suppose that a node at the bottom represents a property which is shared by k poisons; he has a chance of $p_2 = 1/k$ of hitting the correct poison by using only this one tree. The learning scheme discussed in Appendix B should be modified, for more rapid improvement, to specify which additional trees should be consulted to exclude $k - 1$ poisons if the one picked was right and to exclude the one if it was wrong, should the same query or a similar one recur.

We should not, however, constrain the questioner to climb down the tree one node at a time. Let z be the number of levels a questioner can skip in one step; here $0 \leqslant z \leqslant \lambda - 1$. If $z = 0$, he goes down one step or level at a time. If $z = \lambda - 1$, he can go directly to the bottom of the tree in his first question; if the answer fails to pinpoint the poison, he may have to repeat this as many as $k -$ times. On the average, it would take only $(k - 1)/2$ such specific questions. Were he to use with $z = 0$, another tree that could pinpoint the poison uniquely, that tree would need $\lambda = \log_2 k$ levels, and he would have to ask a sequence of that many questions (of increasing specificity).

Let C be the number of comparisons or binary question-answer steps to pinpoint

uniquely an entry in a directory of D entries. If $z = 0$, then $C_{max} = \log_2 D$. To pinpoint an entry to within 1 in k equally likely entries takes $\log_2 D - \log_2 k$ comparisons with $z = 0$. With $z = \lambda - 1$, this takes $(k - 1)/2$ comparisons. If D is large and k is not, then $(k - 1)/2 < \log_2 D - \log_2 k$, and $z = \lambda - 1$ is preferable to $z = 0$.

We interpret z as zoomability. A well-designed directory should allow for variable zoomability. The user (questioner) should be able to make $z = \lambda - 1$ and see in "one glance" (nearly simultaneously) both the entire tree and the bottom nodes, or to make $z = 0$ and see his present step almost simultaneously with his next step. With z high, he can get a global image, which shows the tree in its totality as an integrated unit, indicating how all nodes are interconnected; it enables him to pick goals and subgoals. With z small, he can orient himself locally and chart a short-term course. To use a directory effectively, he needs sometimes to make z large, then small, then again large, etc., in order to converge rapidly to the appropriate unique entry and the appropriate adequate response.

REFERENCES

1. Kruzas, A. T. *Directory of Special Libraries and Information Centers*. Detroit: Gale Research Co., 1963.

2. *Encyclopedia of Information Systems and Services*. Ann Arbor, Mich.: Edwards Bros., 1971.

3. *Directory of Information and Referral Centers*. New York: United Community Funds and Councils of America, Inc., August 1968.

4. Kilgour, F. "Implications for the Future of Reference/Information Service." In *The Present Status and Future Prospects of Reference/Information Service*, edited by W. Linderman. Procedural Conference at Library Service School, Columbia University, 1966. Chicago: American Library Association, 1967.

5. Carnovsky, L., ed. *Library Networks: Promise and Performance*. Chicago: University of Chicago Press, 1969.

6. Swank, R. "Interlibrary Cooperation, Interlibrary Communications and Information Networks: Explanation and Definition." In *Conference on Interlibrary Communications and Information Networks*, edited by J. Becker. Chicago: American Library Association, 1970.

7. Machlup, F. *The Production and Distribution of Knowledge in the United States*. Princeton, N.J.: Princeton University Press, 1962.

8. Martin, L. *Library Response to Urban Change: A Study of the Chicago Public Library*. Chicago: American Library Association, 1969.

9. Rees, A. M. "Libraries and Information Centers." *College and Research Libraries* 25 (May 1964): 200–204.

10. Conant, R. W. "Sociological and Institutional Changes in American Life: Their Implications for the Library." *American Library Association Bulletin* 61 (May 1967): 528.

11. Kahn, A. J. *Neighborhood Information Centers: A Study and Some Proposals*. New York: Columbia University School of Social Work, 1966.

12. Long, N.; Anderson, J.; Burd, R.; Mathis, M. E.; and Todd, S. *Information and Referral Centers: A Functional Analysis*. Minneapolis: Institute for Interdisciplinary Studies, American Rehabilitation Foundation, 1971.

13. Ball, J. "Model Cities Community Information Center." Mimeographed. Philadelphia, 2204 N. Broad Street, 1971.

14. Kochen, M., and Deutsch, K. W. "Toward a Rational Theory of Decentralization: Some Implications of a Mathematical Approach." *American Political Science Review* 63 (September 1969): 734–49.

15. Kochen, M., and Deutsch, K. W. "Decentralization: Coordination and Hierarchy," forthcoming.

16. Stokes, Carl B. *Community Resource Inventory, 1969–1970*. Cleveland: Cleveland Community Development Improvement Program, Office of the Mayor, 1970.

17. Feller, W. *An Introduction to Probability Theory and Its Applications*. Vol. 2. New York: John Wiley & Sons, 1966.

18. Kochen, M. "Referential Consulting Networks." In *Toward a Theory of Librarianship: Festschrift in Honor of J. Shera*, edited by C. Rawski. Cleveland: Case Western Reserve University Press, 1971.

19. Kochen, M. "Cognitive Learning Processes: An Explication." In *Artificial Intelligence and Heuristic Programming*, edited by N. V. Findler and B. Meltzer. Edinburgh: Edinburgh University Press, 1971.

20. Kochen, M. "A Cost-Effectiveness Analysis of See Reference Structure in Directories." *Proceedings of ISLIC*. Mimeographed. Tel Aviv, August 1971.

21. Kochen, M. *Integrative Mechanisms in Literature Growth*. Westport, Conn.: Greenwood Press, 1971.

22. Kochen, M., and Tagliacozzo, R. "A Study of Cross-Referencing." *Journal of Documentation* 24 (September 1968): 173–91.

23. Weik, M. *Standard Dictionary of Computers and Information Processing*. New York: Hayden Book Co., 1969.

24. Doyle, L. B. "Semantic Road Maps for Literature Searches." *Journal of the Association for Computing Machinery*, vol. 8 (October 1961).

25. Rolling, L. *EURATOM Thesaurus* [European Atomic Energy Community Center for Information and Documentation]. Keywords Used within EURATOM's Nuclear Energy Documentation Project. Brussels: Center for Information, 1964.

26. Markowitz, H. M.; Hausner, B.; and

Karr, H. W. *SIMSCRIPT: A Simulation Program Language.* Englewood Cliffs, N.J.: Prentice-Hall, Inc., 1963.

27. Kochen, M. "Switching Centers for Inquiry Referral." In *Procedural Conference on Interlibrary Communications Networks,* edited by J. Becker. Chicago: American Library Association, 1971.

28. Gordon, G. "A General Purpose Systems Simulator." *IBM Systems Journal* 1 (September 1962): 18–33.

29. Reisner, P. "Semantic Diversity and a Growing Man-Machine Thesaurus." In *Some Problems in Information Science,* edited by M. Kochen. Metuchen, N.J.: Scarecrow Press, 1965.

LIBRARY OPERATIONS RESEARCH:
A PROCESS OF DISCOVERY AND JUSTIFICATION

FERDINAND F. LEIMKUHLER

ABSTRACT

This article begins with a discussion of the broad role of operations research (O. R.) in a society undergoing change. The nature of O. R. teams in a library environment is then considered. The function of models in O. R. is analyzed, the development of a model being contrasted with its formal presentation. Criteria for good models are suggested. This article then focuses on storage models for libraries, first considering the Dewey classification system from this perspective and then summarizing more current research carried out under the direction of the author with a grant from the National Science Foundation.

Operations research (O. R.) is the art of using the scientific method to help understand and solve sociotechnical problems. It focuses attention on managerial decision making in times of crisis and change. It did not originate from any "direct heave-ho of poetic strength," as Marshall McLuhan [1] puts it, but as an expedient way for society to adjust to situations in which technologies and cultures are mixed. McLuhan says that "operations research programs the hybrid principle as a technique of creative discovery." Operations research began with the study of military logistics in World War II and has since become an integral part of the military organization. Today, it is flourishing in the industrial world in support of corporate planning and adjustment to the introduction of computer-based management information systems. At the same time, a very substantial beginning has been made in the application of O. R. to the large-scale, complex problems in the public sector. Library O. R. is part of this latter development.

As a creative activity, O. R. can serve an important prophetic role by anticipating future social and technical developments. McLuhan argues that it is very difficult for man to understand the environment in which he lives. Only when new technologies come along and create new cultures do we become aware of the older environment which is replaced, or rather incorporated, into the new one. Man prefers to go into the future looking backward, and as the old is justified in terms of the new, man begins to perceive more fully the structural properties and components of the older environment. The power of the arts to anticipate future cultural developments has long been recognized. McLuhan quotes Ezra Pound, who called the artist "the antennae of the race." By taking a position which is essentially antienvironmental or countercultural, the artist can train his powers of perception and judgment about the nature and implications of environmental change. Today, new technologies and their consequent environments succeed each other in such rapid succession that technology itself is performing the function of art in making us aware of the psychic and social consequences of technological development.

The meeting of two environments in the clash of new and old technologies is a time of action and hybrid energy. It is also a moment of truth and revelation—a particularly favorable time to observe the forces of change in society. In these periods of transition, society needs a science of change, not only to help man to adapt to environmental changes, but, much more important, to help chart and hold a steady course toward more permanent goals, even amidst the most disrupting innovations. McLuhan believes that man is beginning to learn the futility of changing goals in order to accommodate technical change. Operations research is a way of making a systematic inquiry into the problematic relationship between organizational goals and the possibilities of technical innovation.

A TEAM APPROACH

In the field of library and information science a relatively small but substantial beginning has been made, one which has been largely financed with federal support to some libraries—but more often to university professors and their students. For this reason, one might say that libraries have been more useful to O. R. than has O. R. been useful to libraries. University libraries are excellent and convenient laboratories in which to have students develop their skills in this field and to engage in scholarly studies of the managerial and systems-design problems of service organizations and educational institutions. While it is true that this research has not always been directed toward the immediate benefit of the local library, since the researcher may have a mixture of motives and the federal funder may be seeking results of much more general significance, the

quality and relevance of the work that has been done may be as good as, or even better than, the work being done in other areas. What is missing is the presence of more permanent in-house O. R. teams which can concentrate on model implementation as well as model development.

The small, multidiscipline-team approach is an essential feature of O. R., since only a group of men can provide competence in the variety of disciplines and techniques that are needed in the study of broad problems. An in-house team takes on the characteristics of the organization it serves. Thus, when O. R. spread from the military to industry there was a substitution of industrial engineering talent for mechanical engineering, and a substitution of econometricians and other behavioral scientists for physical scientists. At the same time, the military, management, and engineering schools of the country began to develop specialized programs in the field. A typical O. R. team may consist of two scientific types, two engineering types, and one or two people from the behavioral or administrative sciences. They tend to report in a staff capacity to the vice-presidential level of a corporation and are more concerned with long-range planning and development than with day-to-day operations.

It is not obvious what mixture of talent would best serve a library O. R. group. Early experience has shown that people with backgrounds in applied mathematics, statistics, computer science, industrial engineering, the physical sciences, sociology, psychology, and economics can make significant contributions. A five- or six-person team with training in some of these areas and a fair amount of professional library experience should make an excellent beginning. It is difficult, of course, to muster the funds for such ventures, and perhaps most libraries will have to depend on larger organizations for O. R. support, either at the university level or in association with other libraries. The WICHE consortium of universities and colleges [2] supports O. R. and systems-development work on a national level and works closely with applications people at participating institutions. A similar arrangement is being followed for the nine campuses of the University of California in the Library Systems Development Program of the Institute of Library Research [3]. In addition, libraries can secure O. R. services from management consulting groups, but the difficulty in using outside help is the possible lack of understanding, experience, and commitment in the formulation and solution of library-type problems. Thus, it is difficult to escape the need for library professionals to take the initiative in both the direction of O. R. activities and participation in the work itself.

CREDIBILITY

Industrial operations researchers have come to learn that credibility is the major factor in getting support for their work. As Harvey Wagner [4] says, just like pregnancy, there is no such thing as a little credibility. Either an executive believes that the O. R. approach to his problems is valid and useful or he dismisses the whole thing as worthless. Apparently, there are enough managers who are believers and enough operations researchers who are successful and/or cautious, since in a relatively short period of time it is estimated that over half of the major

firms in the United States have established corporate O. R. groups, and that in the next ten years the remaining half are expected to join the ranks of the believers.

Operations research can be a relatively expensive undertaking and it is a long-term, high-risk research investment. For this reason there is a tendency to build an O. R. program slowly around a few carefully chosen studies which will tend to promote confidence within both the group and the organization. Wagner stresses the fact that the O. R. effort must always be directed toward management systems considerations, that is, the results must eventually be integrated into the information, decision-making, and control structure of the organization. The study cannot be undertaken in isolation from the surrounding organizational environment and must ultimately be considered part of a total systems effort. Wagner believes that many O. R. projects fail because it is not realized that implementation must begin on the very first day of the project. The managers who are expected to act on the results must be involved at the start, and the analysts must always be prepared to modify their models in accordance with changes in the organizational environment—changes which the O. R. effort may precipitate.

An important factor leading to misunderstanding and lack of credibility on the part of managers is the language of the discipline. In O. R. the model is the message. Operations research models are problem statements in solution format and therefore are a very precise way of stating a problem. Because the solution is usually a mathematical one, the problems are stated in a highly idealized manner and may not be recognizable to a manager confronting a similar real-world problem. The literature of O. R. follows the custom in science of reporting work in the manner which logically justifies the inferences made. Usually these justifications have little relation to the psychological process by which the really valuable discoveries were made and the essential features of a model were fixed in the analyst's mind. Nevertheless, a model is never fully accepted in O. R. circles until it has been justified in a scientific manner. This means listing the assumptions and deductive steps needed to draw relevant conclusions from the model and giving an orderly description of the design and analysis of experiments aimed at testing hypotheses suggested by the model. Also, a good bit of attention may be given to showing how this model differs from and relates to other models reported in the literature.

MODELING

William Morris [5], in his excellent essay on modeling, points out that many people tend to confuse the ad hoc justification of models in scientific papers with descriptions of the model-building process itself. Morris believes that the process by which an experienced analyst arrives at a model of a management problem is essentially an *intuitive* one. A thorough familiarity with the model literature and the methods of logical justification can be of great help in the discovery process, but it is not a substitute for the creativity needed in model building. Descriptions of the modeling process are hard to find. Analysts learn by doing, and they like to define O. R. as "what O. R. people do." Experienced analysts are reluctant to give much formal at-

tention to this part of their work. They tend to dismiss questions about their choice of variables, environmental factors, and solution techniques as either too trivial to bother with or too nontrivial to be answered. And yet, it is this aspect which is crucial to an understanding and appreciation of O. R. work. Morris tries to be more explicit and suggests three hypotheses about modeling.

1. It is a process of enrichment or elaboration. One begins with a very simple model, quite distinct from reality, and moves toward more elaborate models which more nearly reflect the complexity of the actual management situation. This seems obvious, but it is important and does take a certain amount of poise to confront a complicated problem with a simple model in which one deliberately suppresses consideration of the complicated realities.

2. Analogy and association with similar models and problem situations often determines the starting point in model building. This is why the experienced analyst can often get a head start on the model.

3. Modeling involves two sorts of looping or alternating procedures: (*a*) alternations between modifications of the model and confrontation by data, and (*b*) alternation between exploration of the deductive tractability of the model and the assumptions which characterize it. This is the most important and the hardest part of model building. Striking the proper balance between descriptive realism and mathematical sophistication is no easy trick. It involves a great deal of trial and error and sensitivity testing. The end product is essentially an approximation elaborate enough to capture the essen-

tials yet gross enough to yield computable solutions.

Morris gives several useful tips on modeling, and lists five criteria for good models. These are:

1. *Relatedness* to other O. R. models and techniques.

2. *Transparency* or ease of interpretation; intuitive satisfaction.

3. *Robustness* or sensitivity to the assumptions made.

4. *Fertility* or richness in deductive possibilities.

5. *Ease of enrichment* or ability to modify and expand the model.

Others may quibble over this list, but it serves the purpose of suggesting what modelers are thinking about as they stew over a problem. Obviously this process is not going to yield uniform results in every application. Harvey Wagner notes how he is struck by the way those O. R. experts who have perfected certain modeling techniques are able to tackle almost every problem they encounter with their own specialty, such as linear programming, dynamic programming, queueing theory, etc. He believes their ability to do this—and do it successfully attests more to their personal genius than it does to the flexibility of the techniques they use.

USEFULNESS

In some areas of application there have been enough models developed for the same kind of problem—that it is now possible to practice a little O. R. on O. R. itself; that is, to develop a model for the problem of selecting an O. R. model for solving a problem. Recently, William Souder [6] made such a study of the many models (over forty) which have been proposed for the purposes of allocating resources

among risky research programs. In order to establish criteria and to weigh their importance in evaluating such models, he polled 128 experienced research administrators and management scientists. From this survey, thirty-six significant factors were identified, grouped into five main categories of suitability, and assigned ranks and weights. The five categories, which Souder calls "model features" are as follows (in the rank order of their importance):

1. *Realism* or accuracy in representing real world systems.

2. *Flexibility* or applicability to various kinds of problems.

3. *Capability* to perform various kinds of computational analysis.

4. *Usefulness* or ease of application and comprehension.

5. *Cost* or the expense of setting up and running the model.

The thirty-six criteria associated with these features are listed below.

Realism:
  Multiple objectives
  Multiple constraints
  Orthogonal variables
  Market risk variable
  Technical risk variable
  Manpower limits parameter
  Facility limits parameter
  Budget limits parameter
  Data uncertainty variable
  Premises uncertainty variable

Flexibility:
  Applied projects
  Basic projects
  Priority decisions
  Initiation decisions
  Budget allocation applications
  Project funding applications

Capability:
  Future times analyses
  Optimization analyses
  Simulation analyses
  Selection analyses

Allocation analyses
Scheduling analyses

Usefulness:
Low sensitivity
Familiar variables
Discrete variables
Computer not needed
Special persons not needed
Special interpretation not needed
Low amount of data
Easily obtainable data
Easy to estimate parameters

Cost:
Low setup costs
Low use costs
Low personnel costs
Low computer time
Low data costs

There are some interesting contrasts between Souder's list and Morris's list of model characteristics. Their viewpoint is somewhat different in that Morris is interested in discovery and Souder is more interested in implementation. This may explain why Souder includes "cost," which is always a concern of the manager, and Morris includes "relatedness," which is important to the analyst as a means of validation. Along with deductive arguments and experimental evidence, models need to be subjected to critical review by other analysts, and this is frequently done by establishing relationships among models. Souder does this implicitly when he compares different investment planning models, which are related to one another by the listed thirty-six points of comparison.

Models can be used as efficient devices for processing managerial information, and in this sense O. R. becomes part of the general field of information science with special application to the development of management information systems. In the same way that we can distinguish between the intellec-

tual activities of discovery and justification in the model-building process, it is possible to recognize a similar distinction in the process of model implementation. Justification in this case rests on the crucial question "does it work," or, in the parlance of the system's designer, "is it operational." Operational systems, like polished O. R. models, are media and become part of the technological apparatus of society. Such media, like books, libraries, and computers, are what McLuhan calls "make happen" agents and not "make aware" agents. The fact that they combine to create new environments requires human involvement. This involvement can be relatively passive, making the changes that take place a source of wonder or grief. Or, this involvement can be active and creative if we take the trouble to study the processes of change in order to exercise control over our environment. We can, as McLuhan says, "think things out before we put them out."

BIBLIOGRAPHIC CONTROL

Operations research views the world in a problematic way, that is to say, the content of an O. R. study is the model and the content of a model is a problem related to a technological environment. Problems arise from the efforts of men to exercise control over their environment by creating new technologies or exploiting the ones available. Patrick Wilson [7] defines the library problem as the problem of bibliographic control. "Bibliographic control is a form of power," he says, "power to obtain the knowledge recorded in written form." He argues that bibliographic control is much more than simply locating items of information or being able to line them up and make them march on command. Rather, it is a kind of knowledge about knowledge and, "if knowledge is a form of power, as the familiar slogan claims, bibliographic control is, in a certain sense, power over power." "This mastery," he says, "is not only the knowledge of the contents of texts; it is knowledge of all uses to which texts can be put, by all possible users in all possible circumstances. We shall never in this world have such control; but the ideal is an intelligible one." He footnotes this with a proof of the impossibility of building a "universal bibliographic machine" without ruling out the possibility of machines of limited power.

Granted that bibliographic control, or some limited form of it, is the aim of a library, where does the O. R. analyst begin? He could begin by finding a harried librarian and ask him to describe some problems and see if any lend themselves to mathematical formulation. This is not such a bad way to start as it may seem at first glance. It has the important advantage of motivating the analyst and the librarian to become engaged in a common cause at the outset. There is greater assurance of an initial success. If the analyst starts from a position of mathematical technique alone he runs the risk of having his so-called real-world problem evaporate. It would be better to rely on the hypothesis that, if experienced librarians have not been able to find a satisfying solution to a problem, the answer is not obvious. Furthermore, if the problem is really meaningful to the library environment, then one can be assured that no matter where you start you will begin to converge on the more central issues and problems in library operations. Be-

cause modeling is an evolutionary process of enrichment and elaboration, there is a built-in quest for an ultimate model which will define *the library problem*.

The analyst should eventually consult the large literature on librarianship if only to find justifications for current library practice and arguments against it. For example, it is difficult to proceed far in storage problems without recognizing the influence of great analytic minds like that of Melvil Dewey. The most commonly used book storage system used in American libraries today is based on Dewey's "Decimal Classification and Relative Index" model which he first published in 1876. By drawing on the properties of the mathematical notion of the *real line*, the decimal system is a relatively simple, logical way of arranging items in an orderly, linear way. It makes possible the insertion of an unlimited amount of new materials while maintaining a fixed relationship according to subject matter. The relevance pattern must be a hierarchic one and is dependent on the somewhat arbitrary decision as to which two adjacent items relate most closely to the new one that is inserted between them. It is a testimony to the ingenuity of librarians that they have been able to make this system work so well and so long in the assembling of both small and large collections.

The very practical advantage of the decimal system is that many patrons can and will serve themselves. How well they do this is difficult to ascertain, but it does make it possible for libraries to operate in a largely self-service manner, which has enormous economic advantages. Author and title guides are provided for the user who knows what he wants beforehand and only needs a shelf location or who prefers to browse in that way. Some auxiliary subject cataloging is provided for the patron whose relevance patterns may not match the shelf pattern. This reliance on shelf retrieval has its shortcomings. The user tends to select from what is available since there is no easy way to indicate what is missing. The system does accumulate obsolete, redundant, and mismatched information, and there are no built-in controls for reorganizing a collection so as to better accommodate current user needs and space consideration. In practice, many deliberate violations of the system are made out of necessity and usually in a somewhat arbitrary manner, such as in the shelving of oversized and undersized material, new book collections and old book depositories, and reserve collections and special reference libraries. These kinds of shortcomings and exceptions often provide the best grist for the beginning of an O. R. study in a library.

STORAGE PROBLEMS

One cannot overlook the importance of the scale of operations in justifying an O. R. study. It is a common practice in industry to rely on the big companies to take risks in research and development. A 10 percent savings in cost to a big firm can more than justify the cost of a study, while a small firm would never even consider such a study. This is true in libraries where a relatively small percentage of savings in space and labor could be substantial in absolute terms. The size of large libraries and their space requirements continues to be the most persistent problem in library administration. It is a problem anticipated over

a century ago by the librarian-mathematician Leibnitz when he foresaw whole "cities of books." This was the theme of Fremont Rider's [8] research as librarian at Wesleyan University. Rider spent a lifetime groping with the problems of book storage in libraries, and it is interesting to reread how he reported his findings.

Rider concluded that "no emendations in present library methods alone were going to provide a sufficient solution to our growth problem," and that technical innovations were needed, not for the purpose of replacing the library, but to create a new environment in which the conventional library would be an integral part. With remarkable anticipation of what has become known as the systems approach to problem solving, Rider reported his work in the following manner: "And the reason for our failure to integrate what were really facets of one single problem was that we were blinded by the 'status quo.' We insisted on continuing to accept as library axioms, unalterable and unquestionable, certain assumptions which no longer had validity, such dicta, for instance, as: Libraries are collections of books; books are stored on shelves; library materials have to be cataloged; catalogs have to be made on cards; books must be arranged by their call numbers, etc., etc."

"It is not until we have looked behind, and beyond, every one of these—and many other—supposedly basic axioms of library method, and have seriously questioned their validity as axioms, that we begin to make any real progress. For, when we do this, we are suddenly amazed to find all the mismatched bits of our research library growth puzzle falling, almost of themselves, into a quite astonishingly new synthesis."

Rider's solution was the microcard, forerunner of the present-day microfiche. In this way, he helped discover a new medium which is becoming increasingly important to libraries. However, in looking at his invention in retrospect, it seems that he has preserved the essential character of the conventional library. He proposed organizing a microform library in subject catalog format, just as the conventional library is already in principle an enormous subject catalog of books. In this sense then, Rider's suggestion is essentially a change of scale.

It was only a year after Rider published his work that Vannevar Bush [9] introduced his notions of electronic memory systems using associative rather than hierarchic retrieval schemes, along with some very advanced concepts of miniaturization. His monumental article, "As We May Think," became the blueprint for the new field of information science which precipitated a technological battle between the computer and the book. J. C. R. Licklider [10] says, "One must be prepared to reject not only the schema of the physical library, which is essentially a response to books and their proliferation, but the schema of the book itself, and even that of the printed page as a long term storage device, if one is going to discover the kinds of pro-cognitive systems needed in the future." He does not reject the schema of the computer.

RETRIEVAL PROBLEMS

Contemporary with Rider was the great British documentalist, S. C. Bradford. Bradford [11] focused attention on journals, periodicals, and serials.

Serials storage is a significant departure from the decimal system for monographs. Serials are shelved by title and date of publication and therefore have built-in age control and missing item control. There is greater uniformity of size and ease in predicting shelf requirements. There is also a considerable simplification in the procedures for getting new items on the shelf, an advantage that is looking even more attractive as automatic order systems create bottlenecks in the cataloging procedures for monographs. The importance of this medium is quite evident in the sciences and technology, where it constitutes the bulk of the important literature.

One of the very significant differences between serials and monograph storage is that the problem of bibliographic control is largely the responsibility of the publisher and not the library. Searching in this medium is a chainlike process from item to item, where each item is expected to have its own references to the next one. This is like having the catalog imbedded in the material itself, rather than trying to imbed the material into a catalog. Special retrieval services may be provided as guides to periodicals, but this is almost always done outside the library proper. This freedom from subject classification permits any one serial item, such as a particular journal, to change its subject contents radically over time and still maintain a fixed relative location on the library shelf. The loss of local control is readily apparent when a library attempts to shelve an item in serial form which does not meet the standards of first-rate journals in the provision of bibliographic controls and retrieval services. Such materials are virtually lost the moment they are shelved.

Bradford's study of the periodical literature was aimed at establishing bibliographic control. His institutional solution was the establishment of a national lending library which would be a central depository and clearing-house for most periodicals. Local libraries would hold small selective collections which could even be discarded while depending on the backup services of the central library. The logic for his position rests on his so-called law of scattering, by which he sought to explain why the abstracting services consistently included only about a third of the articles actually published in scientific and technical journals, although the total number of abstracts was about equal to the total number of articles. Bradford was disturbed by the amount of apparent duplication and showed empirically that the recognized articles on any one topic were distributed in a highly skewed manner over the journals publishing them. Thus, trying to see every article on one topic becomes a Herculean task, but to see, say, half of these articles one might only have to search through about 10 percent of the journals carrying such articles. Bradford's model can provide a rich starting point for the study of journal selection problems in a library, or for the distribution of journal holdings over a branch library system, or, on a larger scale, over a network of libraries.

Technological developments going on in the world of librarianship and information science today are greatly enlarging the scope of the problem of bibliographic control and shifting the emphasis from storage and selection to larger problems of information re-

trieval and transfer. These lead to the design and development of information retrieval systems which deliberately refuse to predicate their conceptual plan on the operations of a conventional library. Whether or not this is being done more as an exploratory tactic in the process of discovery or whether it is prophecy of the future remains to be seen. As a technique for discovery, one has to be willing to recognize the need for taking positions which are essentially counterenvironmental in order to test the integrity of that environment. However, as a forecast of the future there may be some comfort in knowing that the time of justification will come for the new technologies too; and in that justification there is an implicit justification for the technology which is superseded.

LIBRARY PROBLEMS

While problems of information awareness, transfer, and retrieval require reference to a much larger system environment, there are many problems which remain within the domain of the local library. Among these are the problems of document selection, storage, and delivery. These are "practical" problems involving the messy realities of limited budgets for acquisitions, buildings with "odd-ball" dimensions and exotic designs, and funders and users with peculiar whims and preferences. Is this the kind of environment in which O. R. can flourish? The answer would seem to depend on the way the library views itself. If it is viewed as something obsolete or just "making do," then the library does not need O. R. If it is seen as a place without options and without goals of its own, then there are no problems of this variety. An alternate and more viable view would see the library as a microcosm of the larger bibliographic world of which it is one of the essential base points. It would seek its justification in the larger environment and not depend solely on its own internal and perhaps obsolete validity. If the library is open, O. R. can be useful. To the O. R. analyst, the problems of the library have not been solved until they are no longer intellectually interesting and no longer socially useful. Certainly, the problems of bibliographic control at the local level do not meet either of those criteria.

Where library O. R. is done as an adjunct to its being taught on the campus, a shotgun approach to problem formulation may result. However, a certain amount of wandering or random searching over the problem field must be expected from any truly creative O. R. effort. This is true of the experience at Purdue University, where I have directed a library operations project over the past six years with support from the National Science Foundation's Office of Science Information Service. Most of the studies made were related to the teaching programs of the university and resulted in masters' theses and doctoral dissertations. However, this work was done as a team effort and in conformity with the objectives of the sponsor and the university library. The library director and his staff were actively engaged in this work both as participants and as reviewers.

The first major study, by Cox [12], was made of book shelving problems. This was followed by a series of related investigations. Raffel [13] perfected Cox's mathematical formulation in order to improve on his solution technique. A subsequent application study in which he compared the model solutions with the actual shelving patterns in three branch libraries at Purdue University was made by Popovitch [14]. O'Neill [15] developed efficient statistical techniques for gathering book shelving data.

The shelving model had implications for several other studies. For example, Roberts [16] demonstrated its relationship to many industrial problems and to models for packaging and cutting steel and paper stock for inventories. He applied it to the design of industrial warehouses. Recently, Ravindran [17] has developed a new solution technique using network or graph theory which greatly expands the model's solution and application capability. An interesting extension was made by Sterling [18], who used the book shelving model to efficiently block MARC II bibliographic record on magnetic computer tapes. Of special significance was the recognition given to the use of these studies in the planning of Princeton University's 500,000-volume auxilliary library.

The concern with library storage problems led directly to studies of depositories by Lister [19] and Mann [20] and of book usage models and retirement policies by Jain [21]. This led also to studies of the Bradford distribution [22] and its application in information search and storage models by Leimkuhler [23] and Baker [24]. O'Neill [25] used this work as a departure point for his study of journal productivity and library organization, and Kraft [26] drew on it in his study of the journal selection problem.

The focus on storage and selection models begged the question: "Is this all there is to a library?" In response

Baker [27] formulated a three-part conception of the library environment based on the behavioral interactions of users, funders, and librarians. Nance [28] simulated this model on a computer and applied it to several branch libraries; Hassel [29] revised the model to include the process of system's design; DeWeese [30] focused on the sociological aspects of the model; and Rzasa [31] studied the problems of goal setting by library managers.

At the outset, the Purdue studies deliberately took a counterenvironmental stance with regard to library automation. That is to say, no attempt was made to justify the use of computers in libraries. Computers were used in all of the studies as a computational or analytic tool but not as an exemplar of futuristic information systems—not initially, anyway. Eventually, the time had to come when this technical dimension had to be considered. This was done in the work of Korfhage and DeLutis [32]. Another expansion of the technological environment has occurred in the studies of the human factors in the use of microform readers by Buck and Lee [33].

Throughout the course of these studies a concerted effort was made to relate the work done to the experience of librarians and other operations researchers, both directly through active participation and indirectly in the literature. The goal, admittedly, was aimed not at the improvement of the Purdue libraries, but toward the improvement of libraries in general by seeking to demonstrate the validity of the O. R. approach through the examples and arguments which would attract the mutual attention and interest of librarians and operations researchers. The fact that the Operations Research Society of America scheduled two sessions at its thirty-eighth national meeting in Detroit (October 1970) and another session at its thirty-ninth meeting in Dallas (May 1971) for the presentation and discussion of library-type models is ample evidence of the professional interest in this subject by analysts. Of equal or perhaps greater importance is the interest being shown by libraries and graduate library schools, as evidenced by the present conference.

REFERENCES

1. McLuhan, Marshall. *Understanding Media: The Extension of Man.* New York: McGraw-Hill Book Co., 1964.
2. Gulko, Warren W. *Program Classification Structure.* Preliminary ed. Boulder, Colo.: Western Interstate Commission for Higher Education, June 1970.
3. Bellomy, Fred. *Organizational Structure of the UC LSD Program.* Report no. LSD 70–38. Santa Barbara: University of California Library Systems Development Program, September 1971.
4. Wagner, Harvey M. *Principles of Operations Research.* Englewood Cliffs, N.J.: Prentice-Hall, Inc., 1969.
5. Morris, William T. *Management Science: A Bayesian Approach.* Englewood Cliffs, N.J.: Prentice-Hall, Inc., 1968.
6. Souder, William E. *Suitability and Validity of Mathematical Models for Research Investment.* Ph.D. dissertation, Saint Louis University, August 1970.
7. Wilson, Patrick. *Two Kinds of Power: An Essay on Bibliographical Control.* Berkeley and Los Angeles: University of California Press, 1968.
8. Rider, Fremont. *The Scholar and the Future of the Research Library.* New York: Hadham Press, 1944.
9. Bush, Vannevar. "As We May Think."

Atlantic Monthly 176 (July 1945): 101–8.

10. Licklider, John C. R. *Libraries of the Future.* Cambridge, Mass.: M.I.T. Press, 1965.

11. Bradford, S. C. *Documentation.* Washington, D.C.: Public Affairs Press, 1950.

12. Cox, J. Grady. *Optimum Storage of Library Materials.* Lafayette, Ind.: Purdue University Libraries, 1964.

13. Raffel, Leslie J. *Compact Book Storage Models.* M.S.I.E. thesis, Purdue University, June 1965.

14. Popovitch, John D. *Compact Book Storage.* M.S.I.E. student project, Purdue University, June 1965.

15. O'Neill, Edward T. *Sampling University Library Collections.* M.S.I.E. thesis, Purdue University, January 1966.

16. Roberts, Stephen D. *Warehouse Size and Design.* Ph.D. thesis, Purdue University, January 1968.

17. Ravindran, Arunachalam. *On Compact Book Storage in Libraries.* Research Memo no. 70-14. Lafayette, Ind.: School of Industrial Engineering, Purdue University, December 1970.

18. Sterling, Keith. *Cost Exchange Analysis of Variable Length versus Fixed Length MARC II Bibliographic Records.* Technical Memo no. 5. Berkeley: University of California Institute of Library Research, April 1969.

19. Lister, Winston C. *Least-Cost Decision Rules for the Selection of Library Materials for Compact Storage.* Ph.D. thesis, Purdue University, January 1967.

20. Mann, Stuart H. *Least-Cost Decision Rules for Dynamic Information Management.* Working paper, Division of Man-Environment Relations, Pennsylvania State University, June 1971. (To appear in *Information Storage and Retrieval.*)

21. Jain, Aridaman K. *A Statistical Study of Book Use.* Ph.D. thesis, Purdue University, January 1968.

22. Leimkuhler, Ferdinand F. "The Bradford Distribution." *Journal of Documentation* 23 (September 1967): 419–27.

23. Leimkuhler, Ferdinand F. "A Literature Search and File Organization Model." *American Documentation* 19 (April 1968): 131–36.

24. Baker, Norman R. "Optimal User Search Sequences and Implications for Information Systems Operation." *American Documentation* 20 (July 1969): 203–12.

25. O'Neill, Edward T. *Journal Usage Patterns and Their Implications in the Planning of Library Systems.* Ph.D. thesis, Purdue University, January 1970.

26. Kraft, Donald H. *The Journal Selection Problem in a University Library System.* Ph.D. thesis, Purdue University, January 1971.

27. Baker, Norman R. "A Descriptive Model of Library/User/Funder Behavior in a University Environment." *Drexel Library Quarterly* 4 (January 1968): 16–30.

28. Nance, Richard E. *Strategic Simulation of a Library/User/Funder System.* Ph.D. thesis, Purdue University, June 1968.

29. Hassel, H. Paul. *An Analytical Design Framework for Academic Library System Formulation.* Ph.D. thesis, Purdue University, 1968.

30. DeWeese, L. Carroll, III. *Status Concerns and Professionalization among Librarians.* M.S. thesis, Purdue University, January 1969.

31. Rzasa, Philip V. *The Development of Measures of Effectiveness for a University Library.* M.S.I.E. thesis, Purdue University, June 1969.

32. Korfhage, Robert R., and DeLutis, Thomas G. *A Basis for Time and Cost Evaluation of Information Systems.* Research Memo no. 69-6. Lafayette, Ind.: School of Industrial Engineering, Purdue University, June 1969.

33. Lee, David R., and Buck, James R. *An Evaluation of Selected Parameters at the Microform Reading Man-Machine Interface.* Ph.D. thesis proposal, Purdue University, December 1970.

AN OPERATIONS RESEARCH STUDY OF A VARIABLE LOAN AND DUPLICATION POLICY AT THE UNIVERSITY OF LANCASTER[1]

MICHAEL K. BUCKLAND

ABSTRACT

The Library Research Unit of the University of Lancaster used an Operations Research (O. R.) approach to recommend changes in loan and duplication policies in the university library. The "variable" loan and duplication policy which was developed is described and also the considerable impact of implementation. Other libraries are now adopting this kind of policy. The work is presented as a case study in library O.R. The great importance of analyzing the structure of problems is stressed and the nature and usefulness of models is described. For the most useful results, suitable librarians should be included in the research team.

A library is a growing organism.　　[RANGANATHAN, *Fifth Law*]

The research and development activity within the University of Lancaster Library has concentrated on exploring, analyzing, and describing the interactions which take place in the provision and use of library services with the aim of providing an improved basis for making decisions about the way the library service is provided [1]. One of the topics we examined a few years ago was that of stock control—more specifically, loan and duplication policies. This has been chosen as a case study because it illustrates rather well the problems and possibilities of applying an O. R. approach in a library.

THE PROBLEM AREA DESCRIBED

During the winter of 1968 the university librarian felt dissatisfied with loan policies in force at that time.

There had been complaints, and a "frustration survey" had shown that the main reason why users failed to find books was that they were out on loan at the time [2]. He therefore directed his research unit to examine the problem of loan policies and to prepare recommendations.

Every library has a loan policy of some kind, even if it is that no books may be removed from the library. University libraries commonly have several policies: some material may be confined to the library, some may be borrowed from a reserve collection for a few hours, the remainder usually for a longer period—the length of time permitted depending on the status of the borrower. Furthermore, there are also wide variations from library to library in terms of length of loan period, renewal policies, fine rates, and the administration of overdues.

This variety (and, indeed, changeability) seems to stem from the complex conflicts of interest involved and it is necessary to try to disentangle

[1] The work of the Library Research Unit was initiated and fostered by the university librarian, A. Graham Mackenzie. This case study would not have been completed without the O. R. expertise of Dr. A. Hindle. The encouragement and support of the Office of Scientific and Technical Information and the Council on Library Resources are gratefully acknowledged.

these and examine the structure of the problem.

1. For the individual borrower a long loan period is desirable because it gives him greater freedom to retain a book at leisure without being bothered by overdue notices, fines and the need to bring it back. Another borrower might ask the library to recall this book, but this may not happen very often. He is, of course, quite free to return the book early—as soon as he has finished with it—but a long loan period is definitely more convenient for the individual borrower.

2. For everybody else this borrower's lengthy loan period is *inconvenient,* because there is always some probability that someone else may want that particular book. The longer the borrower retains it, the longer it is absent from the shelf and the less chance anyone else has of finding it immediately available when they want it. For everyone except the borrower, a *shorter* loan period is more convenient. The fact that every library user plays both the role of borrower and the role of "everybody else" does not remove this conflict of interest.

Now, although books can be made more readily available by inducing borrowers to retain them for relatively short periods only, five further complications arise.

3. The level of demand varies enormously from book to book or, to put it another way, the probability that a book will be sought while it is out on loan varies greatly. There is little justification for curtailing the loan of material which is unlikely to be asked for, but for material known to be in heavy demand there is a very good case for wanting borrowers to return their books quickly if the frustration of other would-be borrowers is to be minimized. It does not make the librarian's task any easier that the probability that another reader will seek a book is not easy to assess.

4. Inducing the borrower to return a book soon is not the only way of reducing the frustration of other would-be borrowers because one can always provide another copy. Duplication is clearly an acceptable alternative strategy. However, it must be noted that although shorter loan periods and additional copies both increase the chances that a copy will be on the shelf, these policies differ in two important respects. First, shorter loan periods are definitely less convenient for the individual borrower, and to this extent undesirable. Second, the provision of duplicate copies uses up money and labor which the library could well have used for other purposes, such as another, *different* title. To this extent, duplication is also undesirable. The policy of providing different titles as deliberate alternatives in the event of failure to find the book originally sought is difficult to assess because little seems to be known about the "substitutability" of titles, especially in an academic environment.

5. If a book is not on the shelf then it can still be made available by means of a reservation and, if appropriate, by recalling it from the reader who has it. To the extent to which this is an acceptable substitute for immediate availability on the shelf, this arrangement reduces the importance of "immediate availability," and thereby permits longer loan periods and less duplication. Acceptability apart, this cumbersome procedure of reservation and recall is clearly unsuitable for those who are not seeking a specific title, but

are browsing, perhaps purposefully, for inspiration or amusement. If such a reader is browsing along the shelves, then it is clearly important that appropriate material should be on the shelves. Otherwise, unless he also browses in the catalogs, the reader will remain unaware of the existence of suitable material and the provision of procedures for reservation and recall will be irrelevant.

6. Administrative aspects must also be considered, since not all loan and duplication policies are equally easy to administer.

7. Similarly, it is essential to consider political aspects. It is not enough to devise loan and duplication policies: they have to be acceptable to the public served. In libraries, as in other public services, the users are, indirectly, the policy makers. It can be argued quite plausibly that the widespread practice of allowing more liberal loan privileges to faculty members than to undergraduates stems more from the power structure of universities than from any attempt by librarians to manage their resources effectively.

It will be quite clear from these observations that the wide variations in loan and duplication policies reflect quite complicated relationships involving a number of conflicting objectives. Any rational loan and duplication policy must be a considered compromise.

In order to clarify the roles of the various factors, the researchers at Lancaster adopted the strategy of relating each factor to the chances that a reader would find a copy of a bok on the shelves when he wanted it. This can properly be regarded as a measure of library performance. We called it "satisfaction level." Apart from the number of copies held, the two critical

factors determining the satisfaction level of any given document are (1) the frequency with which the book is sought (its popularity); and, (2) the length of time it is off the shelves when used.

The basic relationship is in the following form:

a) *For any given loan period,* the chances of a reader finding on the shelves a copy of the book he seeks varies inversely with the popularity. The greater the popularity, the lower the satisfaction level; the less the popularity, the higher the satisfaction level (see fig. 1).

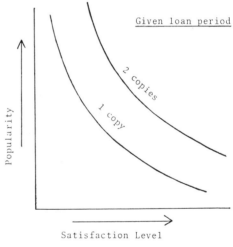

FIG. 1

b) *For any given popularity,* the length of the loan period and the satisfaction level are inversely related. The longer the loan period, the lower the satisfaction level; the shorter the loan period, the higher the satisfaction level (see fig. 2).

c) *For any given satisfaction level,* the popularity and the length of the loan period are necessarily also inversely related. The greater the popularity, the shorter the loan period has

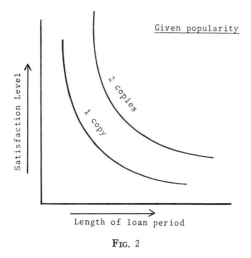

FIG. 2

to be; the less the popularity, the longer the loan period can be (see fig. 3).

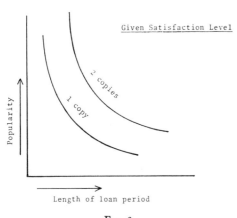

FIG. 3

d) Increasing the number of copies available, like shortening the length of loan periods, increases satisfaction level. To this extent, it is an alternative strategy. The relationship can be seen in figures 1–3 by comparing the curve for one copy with the curve for two copies.

These relationships have been described in some detail because they lead to a most significant conclusion.

If the library is intended to make documents available and if promptness is a virtue, then *the cardinal rule of library stock control is that both the loan period and the duplication policy should be related to the level of demand for the title and to each other.*

In presenting this case study, the careful analysis and description of the problem area has been stressed not only because it sets the scene but also because this process constitutes the first and possibly the most important feature of the O. R. approach. A significant aspect of this systems analysis is the pinpointing of the need to develop measures of performance where these do not already exist.

MEASUREMENT

Exploring the structure of a problem is a necessary first stage in O. R. It is also necessary to make measurements and calculations in order to add proportion and precision to the relationships which have been perceived in a rather subjective manner—and, at some stage, their validity needs to be checked. It is at this stage that the skill of the professional librarian in collecting data and the technical mathematical expertise of the professional O. R. scientist become important. The details of the data collection and the calculations involved in this case study have been reported elsewhere [3, 4] and need only be summarized briefly here.

DATA COLLECTION

In addition to the collection of data relating to the way in which demand was spread over the book stock, surveys relevant to two neglected aspects of librarianship were made.

1. What effect does the official loan

period have on the length of time books are kept out? Circulation data from a number of universities showed that there is a marked tendency for books to be kept out until they are due back. There was little evidence that the status of the borrower or the subject matter of the book had any relevance.

2. What effect does the official loan period have on the frequency of renewal? It had been suggested that if loan periods were reduced in an attempt to increase satisfaction level, the users would respond by renewing their loans more often. If so, the time the book is off the shelves would remain the same. Satisfaction level would remain unchanged and a great deal of bureaucratic inconvenience would have been caused to library and user alike. Data on the actual frequency of renewal in various circumstances indicated that the great majority of loans were not renewed and that the status of the borrower, the subject matter of the book, and the length of the official loan period had little effect on the frequency of renewal.

These findings are highly significant. *They mean that the librarian has, in his ability to determine official loan periods, a powerful and precise control device for influencing the availability of the books in his library.* They permit us to predict how long books will be kept out under any given loan policy.

CALCULATION

By this time the necessary ingredients were available for making some numerical calculations. These were done in three stages:

1. The proportion of books at various levels of demand was estimated from circulation data. This had predictable affinities with the Bradford-Zipf distribution which seems to pervade library matters [5, 6].

2. The precise effect on satisfaction level had to be computed for any given combination of (*a*) length of loan, (*b*) amount of in-library use, (*c*) number of copies, and (*d*) probability that a reader will ask for it to be reserved or recalled if he cannot find it for each level of demand. Table 1 illustrates the form of result which emerged.

There are at least two ways of performing these particular calculations. At Lancaster they were done by simulating the borrowing process repeatedly on a computer to see what happened (Monte Carlo simulation). Morse has described in some detail how they can be done analytically by means of queuing theory [7]. Either way, this illustrates another essential feature of O. R. These most useful calculations could only be done by means of a *model* of the process involved. In the one case, this model is a logic diagram flow charting what could happen and used in conjunction with various estimates

TABLE 1

ESTIMATED SATISFACTION LEVELS FOR VARIOUS COMBINATIONS OF LOAN PERIOD, DEGREE OF DUPLICATION, AND LEVELS OF POPULARITY (%)

OFFICIAL LOAN PERIOD	No. OF COPIES	ESTIMATED SATISFACTION LEVEL FOR BOOKS AT EACH OF FIVE LEVELS OF POPULARITY				
		A	B	C	D	E
5 weeks	1	52	62	72	82	97
5 weeks	2	84	91	97	99	100
1 week	1	90	94	98	99	100

of the chances that what might happen will happen. In the other case, the model is in the form of algebraic equations in which the values of various factors can be varied experimentally. *Without such models, one cannot predict the consequences of hypothetical changes and the data collection would be a much more sterile exercise.*

3. Given an estimate of the effect of any particular loan and duplication policy on material at each popularity level, and given an estimate of the amount of material at each popularity level, the overall satisfaction level of the library as a whole could be estimated. The University of Lancaster Library was estimated to have had a satisfaction level of about 60 percent during the session 1967–68. In other words, we judged that a user seeking open-shelf material was finding it about six times out of ten. The impact that a selection of other loan and duplication policies would have had on satisfaction level was also estimated.

So far discussion has been in terms of users seeking specific items. Since users also browse more or less purposefully, the effects of loan and duplication policies on the quality of service provided for browsers was also examined. Let us consider what happens when the user of a typical university library browses rather vaguely for "something on economics." What are the characteristics of the array of documents available on the shelves? First, the library staff will probably have removed all the strongly recommended books and put them in a reserve collection—perhaps on closed access. Second, other recommended or popular books are likely to be out on loan. Those which are little recommended and little used, however, are much

more likely to be present. In brief, the array of documents made available to the browser is likely to be systematically biased toward the least recommended and the least used. This "collection bias" can be measured readily in terms of, for example, the 10 percent most popular books which are off the shelves at any given time. At Lancaster, at that time, there were three return dates a year for undergraduates and one only for postgraduates and teaching staff. We estimated that 45 percent of these popular books would be off the shelves. Since the effect of alternative loan and duplication policies on the satisfaction level of material at each popularity level can be estimated, the impact on collection bias could also be assessed.

Other calculations were used to assess the administrative costs likely to be incurred by alternative policies, but these were subsidiary to the critical element. This was the indispensable use of a model to predict what would have happened with other policies without having to actually implement them experimentally.

DECISION

The effects of the policies then in force had been analyzed in terms of satisfaction level, collection bias, and administrative cost, and compared with the effects of a selection of alternative policies. In order to reach a decision, it was necessary to make a series of value judgments concerning the relative importance of these measures and other relevant factors. For example, if satisfaction level were at 60 percent, by how much ought it to be increased and at what point would improvement become too expensive?

As a basis for informed judgment,

the research unit prepared a memorandum for the librarian, setting forth alternative ways of raising satisfaction level to about 80 percent and reducing collection bias to 20 percent or less. These included:

A. No change in loan policies but enough systematic duplication to achieve the desired standards. Estimated cost of duplication £10,000–£15,000 ($24,000–$36,000) initially and £2,000 ($4,800) recurrently.

B. Staff and graduate students, four return dates a year; undergraduates, two weeks; renewals permitted. Although traditional, policies based on the status of the borrower are rather inefficient from the point of view of stock control—and, arguably, inequitable. This particular policy would have achieved an estimated satisfaction level of 73 percent and a collection bias of 32 percent.

C. A variable loan policy, whereby the most popular books are subject to a shorter loan period regardless of the status of the borrower. Numerous permutations are possible. One was that about 10 percent of the stock should be subject to a one-week loan period, the rest would have four return dates a year. This was expected to raise satisfaction level to 86 percent and reduce collection bias to 8 percent.

After intensive discussion of both principles and practicalities, the librarian prepared a revised memorandum[2] for the university's Library Committee, which approved his recommendation that the variable loan period be adopted whereby about 10 percent of the stock would be subject to a one-week loan period. The loss of faculty privilege,

the avoidance of high expenditure on duplication as in solution A, the expected improvement in the standards of library service, and doubts about whether the change would be acceptable, were all considered.

Although this O. R. study had analyzed and quantified the issues involved to an unprecedented degree, the decision-making process still involved subjective judgments. The contribution of the study had been to provide better information on many, but not all, of the issues involved.

CONTROL

A number of administrative changes had to be made in order to implement the new system. The key problem was that of deciding which books were the most popular ones. It was decided to base decisions directly on past usage as recorded on the date label attached inside each book, as suggested by Fussler and Simon [8]. Clerical labor "monitored" 70,000 monographs and, if appropriate, reprocessed them with distinctive markings. This took $2\frac{1}{2}$ days and cost £110 ($264) plus supervision.

A particularly important feature of a variable loan and duplication policy of this type is that it presupposes repeated monitoring at intervals to ensure that the items made subject to a one-week loan period are in fact the most popular ones. This has a significance which goes far beyond the reluctant acceptance of yet another clerical routine, because the recurrent monitoring of the stock is in effect a matter of using feedback to make the library provision continuously responsive to changes in the pattern of demand. In engineering terminology, this constitutes a self-adaptive stock control system. If the demand on a particular section of the library increases, then the proportion of material subject to a one-week loan will increase, thereby maintaining satisfaction level and collection bias, albeit at a cost in terms of increased inconvenience through an increased proportion of one-week loans. As the popularity of a section declines, the proportion of material subject to a one-week loan period also declines, to the greater convenience of the reduced number of users who still borrow from this section.

Duplication policies are inseparable from loan policies and merge particularly well in the context of a variable policy. The effect of increasing the number of copies is to reduce the level of demand on each copy, which in turn determines the loan period for that copy. A situation of steadily rising demand would be signaled by an increase in the proportion of books subject to a one-week loan period and in the proportion of borrowings which is for material subject to a one-week loan period. If the librarian considered that these proportions were becoming higher than was suitable for the convenience of his users, then he could increase his expenditure on duplicates. This would have the effect of reducing the level of demand on individual copies and thereby eventually reducing the proportion of one-week borrowing. In this manner the librarian has a continuous and objective indication of the adequacy of duplication in relation to specified standards of service. Furthermore, titles suitable for duplication can be identified during the monitoring process.

This illustrates the key concept of feedback, which needs to develop in step with automation. An automated circulation control system harnessed to a policy of this kind and a clear concept of management information would be much more than an electronic location indicator.

IMPACT

Implementation of the new policy was followed by a dramatic increase in library use. After six months, a survey of users' opinions revealed a widespread opinion that the effects had been good. After one year, the stock was extensively remonitored to adapt to the large increase in demand. This was followed by a further substantial increase in library use. It may be a few years before provision and demand stabilize. It should be stressed that library use per capita had always been unusually high, nonetheless borrowing from the open shelves has increased by 200 percent over two years, although the user population had only increased by 40 percent.

Since an increase of this magnitude had not been expected, it highlighted a gap in our understanding of user behavior. The calculations had not allowed for it: the models were incomplete. This has lead the research unit to concentrate much more on the development of more detailed models of user behavior. This is necessary if library-user interactions are to be better understood.

A feature of O. R. is that there is considerable emphasis on explicit, objective description. This facilitates the communication and, therefore, the impact of ideas. So far four British university libraries have announced the adoption of a variable policy for some or all of their collections.

REFLECTIONS ON O. R.
IN LIBRARIES

Five years of active involvement in this type of work at the Lancaster University Library Research Unit leads naturally to a number of reflections on O. R. in libraries and the relationships between librarians and professional O. R. scientists. The views expressed are highly personal ones. The viewpoint is that of a librarian based inside a library but privileged to be working with O. R. experts.

The key problem lies in analyzing the structure of library problems. Without this little progress can be made. The *responsibility* for doing this rests entirely on the shoulders of the librarian. It is the essence of management in a library, as elsewhere, *but* a professional O. R. expert, especially one with previous experience of O. R. in social services, can make an enormous contribution as a stimulus and catalyst in clarifying the issues involved. This is the most important role of a professional O. R. expert and can, in itself, have remarkable consequences [9]. The sophisticated mathematical techniques associated with O. R. play a less important role. Every project needs access to this expertise but it is not always needed and can hinder effective dialogue between O. R. experts and librarians.

The personality of the chief librarian is important, since O. R. recommendations are unlikely to be satisfactorily implemented unless the chief librarian is not only genuinely anxious to improve his services but also capable of appreciating an analytical approach to his problems.

The knowledge of competent librarians is also useful in describing library problems to the O. R. team and in advising on methods of data collection.

If the work is to be useful, a mixed research team of librarians and others is appropriate. Librarians working in this role definitely need to be capable of analyzing problems. They do not have to be expert in the mathematical techniques, however. For the most useful results, librarians ought to constitute about half of those actively engaged in the research, as opposed to persons in an advisory or liaison capacity. This judgment stems from three considerations:

1. A significant element of librarianship is likely to help keep the research in touch with library realities and the reports intelligible to the library profession.

2. This element is likely to act as an antidote to motivations on the part of professional O. R. scientists which could deflect the research from actually being useful. Such motivations include the need to provide funding and points of departure for technical dissertations by O. R. students. Also there is the desire to develop highly sophisticated papers for the O. R. press which may improve their author's reputation more than his library service.

3. Most important is the question of manpower. Working on an O. R. project is an excellent training. All too often O. R. specialists who have acquired experience in library planning problems move on to other pastures, such as transportation, computers, or industrial problems, and the expertise is lost. In contrast, a librarian with this experience is likely to remain in librarianship and to continue to contribute to library problems. In the long

term, this absorption of experience may in itself be more beneficial to libraries than the original project was. In a sense, projects staffed entirely by O. R. specialists can have a preemptive, even stultifying, effect on the library profession which has little enough expertise in effective management anyway.

In the context of research and development in librarianship and in comparison with, say, classification research, historical bibliography, and computerization, research of an O. R. type into basic planning and management problems seems to offer the best prospects, at least in the short term, of enabling librarians to improve the library services for which they are responsible. The best kind of self-confidence and professionalism is that which stems from a better informed and more quantitative understanding of the nature of the complexities in the provision and use of library services—of the library as a growing organism.

REFERENCES

1. Mackenzie, A. Graham. "Library Research at the University of Lancaster." *Library Association Record* 73 (1971): 91–92.
2. Buckland, M. K., et al. *Systems Analysis of a University Library: Final Report on a Research Project.* University of Lancaster Library Occasional Papers, no. 4. Lancaster: University of Lancaster, 1970.
3. American Library Association. Library Administration Division. Circulation Control Committee. *Circulation Policies of Academic Libraries in the United States, 1968.* Chicago: American Library Association, 1970.
4. Buckland, M. K., and Hindle, A. "Loan Policies and Duplication." In *Planning Library Services: Proceedings of a Research Seminar,* edited by A. G. Mackenzie and I. M. Stuart. University of Lancaster Library Occasional Papers, no. 3. Lancaster: University of Lancaster, 1969.
5. Buckland, M. K., and Hindle, A. "Library Zipf." *Journal of Documentation* 25 (1969): 52–57.
6. Fairthorne, R. A. "Empirical Hyperbolic Distributions (Bradford-Zipf-Mandelbrot) for Bibliometric Description and Prediction." *Journal of Documentation* 25 (1969): 319–43.
7. Morse, P. M. *Library Effectiveness: A Systems Approach.* Cambridge, Mass.: M.I.T. Press, 1968.
8. Fussler, H. H., and Simon, J. L. *Patterns in the Use of Books in Large Research Libraries.* Chicago: University of Chicago Library, 1969.
9. Ackoff, R. L. "A Black Ghetto's Research on a University." *Journal of the Operations Research Society of America* 18 (1970): 761–71.

LIBRARY OBJECTIVES AND PERFORMANCE MEASURES AND THEIR USE IN DECISION MAKING[1]

MORRIS HAMBURG, LEONARD E. RAMIST, AND MICHAEL R. W. BOMMER

ABSTRACT

For optimal allocations of limited funds, it is necessary for libraries to develop measures of output. Various forms of user exposure to documents are discussed in an effort to develop such measures for public libraries. It is suggested that the accrual method of accounting be used to compare such measures with costs, and an illustrative computation is presented. It is shown how size of user population, amount of exposure, and costs for a given year can be estimated. Similar techniques are suggested for evaluation of library programs. This approach is then compared with current concepts of library standards. The paper concludes with suggestions for further research.

Libraries, as all other institutions and organizations in the public and private sectors, are faced with the economic problem of allocating their limited resources in such a manner as to generate maximum benefits. Correspondingly, the institutions from which libraries derive their resources are faced with similar allocation issues. To allocate resources effectively, these units must know what their objectives are. Furthermore, they should be able to measure their performance or degree of achievement of objectives. These are the basic problems of management at any level.

In recent years, the general management problems of libraries have been accelerating at a dizzy pace. Rapid expansion has taken place in development of cooperative arrangements among libraries, in computerization, mechanization, and centralization of library services; in sizes of collections; and in the variety of services offered by libraries. These increasing complexities of library organizational arrangements and expansions in activities and services make it all the more important for libraries to define their objectives clearly and to have methods for measuring the level of attainment of these objectives.

The research project, of which the work reported here represents a part, has been concentrating on the problem of statistical information systems which would provide quantitative information for effective management of university and large public libraries. It appears to us that there is an inseparable need not only for improved library statistical data systems but also for frameworks for rational decision making concerning library operations and resources. Therefore, our orienta-

[1] The research on which this paper is based is part of a project on "The Development of Statistical Information Systems for University and Large Public Libraries." This research has been supported by the U.S. Office of Education under contract number OEG-0-8-080802-4687(095). Prof. Morris Hamburg is director of the project, which is being carried out at the Wharton School, University of Pennsylvania. The other two authors are research associates on the study and are writing doctoral dissertations in this area of research. The project expresses appreciation for assistance received from government officials, library directors, librarians, officials of library associations, research workers, and others.

tion has been to devote considerable effort to the development of analytical models which might assist library administrators in making decisions which would maximize the flow of benefits imparted to the communities the library serves. These models also focus on the problem of the optimum allocation of funds among library service efforts and among library units. The basic reason for this approach is the concept that the essential purpose of any information system is to convey relevant information to decision makers. The work reported on in this paper represents some suggestions on possible performance measures which can be incorporated into the aforementioned analytical models.

Of course, any attempts to define library objectives and to measure performance and the benefits and costs of alternative courses of action concerning library services encounter a host of theoretical and practical difficulties. However, the pressures for making such determinations are increasing. Doubtlessly, it is true that all public or social institutions and their component parts are currently competing for limited funds, and in this context are under increasing pressure not only to specify their needs or required "inputs," but to indicate in some meaningful and measurable way, what their "outputs" are. It is in the spirit of attempting to suggest some aids in this difficult task that the work reported on here was carried out.

In this paper, we review recorded objectives of public and university libraries and we attempt to convert these objectives into explicit statements of purpose. We propose and evaluate some alternative measures for determining library performance and

give illustrations of their computation and use. Finally, we comment briefly on library standards and offer some suggestions regarding areas for future research.

LIBRARY OBJECTIVES

There is a great variety of written statements identifying both public library and university library objectives. For public libraries, these statements relate to both formal and informal education. Under formal education, the emphasis is upon the supplementation, enrichment, and further development of educational programs of schools and colleges. Under informal education, the objectives emphasize the library materials, the process of communicating with the user, or the end result of library use.

Recorded objectives which relate specifically to library materials emphasize variety in subject matter, point of view, and media; the meeting of research needs; good organization of materials to make them easily and temptingly available; and good distribution of materials. Examples of objectives referring to the process of communicating with the user are: encouraging reading of socially significant materials; interpreting materials; expressing ideas; providing information; and entering into the educational, civic, and cultural activities of community groups. Finally, many recorded objectives relate to the end result of library use: individual self-development, increasing reading enjoyment and ability, human understanding, better family and community members, aid in daily occupations, consumer and health education, creative use of leisure time, culture, and creative and spiritual capacities.

Although the objectives and ultimate benefits of a university library are quite similar to those of a public library, there are some distinctive differences. First, the population of potential users of a university library is relatively more homogeneous and operates at higher intellectual and reading levels than the public at large. Indeed, the public library has such a heterogeneous population of potential users that it includes university students and faculty, as well as, for example, the disadvantaged groups.

Second, whereas the public library responds to the societal objectives of the entire community, the university library is an integral part of a small subset of that community, namely, the university. Hence, the university library's objectives must relate to those of the parent university.

The objectives of a university are generally stated in terms of the functions it performs in the areas of instruction, research, and community service. Since the university library supports university programs, objectives for the university library should be in terms of the needs and requirements of the personnel involved in the teaching and research efforts of the university concerned.

A statement adopted by the ACRL (Association of College and Research Libraries) Board of Directors represents a basis for a workable objective. It reads: "The primary purpose of any library is to serve the *reading, reference and research needs of its users*. All authorized users of college and research libraries have a right to expect library services up-to-date and commensurate with their needs, provided by competent librarians and founded on adequate collections which are easily available in suitable quarters" [1].

As was true for the analogous statements of objectives for public libraries, this type of statement is not sufficiently explicit to be of direct assistance to management in the planning and decision-making process. Further analysis is required to develop an objective which is both explicit and measurable in order that library performance may be evaluated in terms of the degree of objective attainment.

DEVELOPMENT OF LIBRARY PERFORMANCE MEASURES

The major difficulty concerning the stated public and university library objectives is that they do not yield criteria for evaluating alternative policies. They are not helpful in determining how well the library is performing nor how proposed plans and alternative decisions may affect this performance.

Clearly, there would be serious problems involved in any attempt to measure these objectives and to associate them with library programs. For example, how do we measure individual self-development? Even if it were possible to discern specific changes in the reading abilities of the disadvantaged or in the cultural, creative, and spiritual capacities of the general population served by a public library, how much of these changes could be attributed to the effect of the library, compared with other social institutions? Analogous questions can be raised concerning each library objective in the aforementioned statement, for both public and university libraries.

Furthermore, even if we could measure the stated objectives, we would face serious difficulties in using these measures as criteria for evaluating library programs. This difficulty results from the interrelatedness of the objectives and the conflict between them.

As an example of the interrelatedness of objectives, it may be noted that a particular book may serve a variety of purposes to the same person or to different people. For one person, the book might represent an important personal growth experience. For another, it might significantly affect his individual and group activities. To yet another, it may be relaxing leisure-time activity. Also, the book may affect one person in all of these ways. The problem created by this interdependence of objectives for measures of performance is primarily one of allocation. For example, suppose a new library program were introduced and we wished to measure its performance in terms of the statements of objectives. Assume the new program resulted in increased library usage. In view of the interdependence of the objectives, how much achievement of each of the objectives was brought about by the new program? The measurement difficulties are only too clear.

The conflict between objectives also poses problems of quantitative measurement. For example, there is conflict between objectives such as provision of library materials and personal communication to potential users. The conflict is present because investment in library materials competes with investment in library staff for the library's scarce funds. Hence, a library program which would attempt to maximize the degree of attainment of only one of these objectives would be failing to maximize the level of attainment of the other. Another conflict is created by the implied objective of providing library services at the lowest possible cost, thereby keeping investment in both library materials and staff as low as possible.

The immediate benefits attributed to satisfaction of the reading, reference, and research needs of university library users and attributed to fulfillment of each of the informal and formal education objectives of the public library are the intangibles of educational endeavors: knowledge, ability, creativity, motivation, and confidence. The ultimate benefits of this investment in intangibles include progress toward the fulfillment of *all* societal objectives, involving every aspect of human endeavor. The real outputs of library service are the stimulated student or teacher, the scientific discovery, the informed voter, the successful businessman, etc. Although the library contributes to all societal objectives, it is only one of several institutions which contribute to any single objective of society.

In developing a library performance measure, ideally we would like to measure the library effect on societal objectives. However, it is an insurmountable task to isolate library effects from those of other institutions.

It is necessary to step back in order to measure these ultimate benefits in a less direct, but perhaps more feasible, manner. Rather than to attempt to analyze the interface between library users and society, a more reasonable approach is to focus on the interface between the library and its population of potential users. A possibility is to measure the library educational effects on knowledge, ability, creativity, motivation, and confidence. However, here too it is difficult to isolate library effects from effects of formal educational institutions, the family, peers, and the community. Also, since each use of a library tends to have a particular purpose, educational measurement in libraries would be much more difficult than in formal educational institutions.

Taking one more small step back from ultimate benefits, we focus upon the *sine qua non* of library activity, the most important aspect of all public and university library objectives— *exposure of individuals to documents of recorded human experience.* Figure

Direct exposure is the result of certain library transactions, some of which are typically recorded and others are not. An individual may take a document from its storage location or charge it out from a reserve room in order to use it in the library. He may charge it out from general circulation or make photocopies in order to use it either in the library or outside. Finally, he may obtain a document by means of interlibrary loan.

Indirect exposure occurs when a library employee communicates to an individual as a substitute for direct

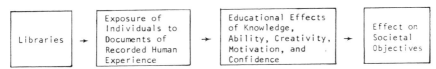

FIG. 1.—Analysis of library benefits

1 illustrates how this exposure is two steps removed from the ultimate library effect on societal objectives. "Document" is used throughout this report to include all library material regardless of form, except for indexes or catalogs, which are used primarily to locate and identify documents.

Exposure can occur either directly or indirectly, in the library or outside the library, in the short run or in the long run. Direct exposure occurs when it would appear to a reasonable third party that the individual in question is applying at least one of his senses— seeing, hearing, or touching (tasting and smelling seem inappropriate at our present levels of communication)—to a document. For example, if he is sitting with a book open in front of him, there is direct exposure. Other examples are observing a picture, watching a film, listening to a recording, and touching Braille.

exposure. Examples are the answering of an informational request, either in person or by telephone, or a storytelling session for children.

Not all library activity is designed to bring about immediate exposure. Some activity may be described as investment in future exposure, similar to business investment in capital expenditures, goodwill, and prepaid expenses. Some examples are purchasing and processing documents which are to be used sometime in the future, and promoting the use of the library, which may result in converting nonusers to users.

A number of serviceable concepts of library objectives involving the idea of exposures can be constructed. One useful conceptualization of library objectives is to maximize document exposure (direct or indirect, in the library or outside the library, in the short run or in the long run) per dollar of input expenditures (costs) used to obtain these exposures. Alternatively, if an imputed dollar value of exposures is derived, then another useful way of viewing library objectives is to maximize the difference between this value of exposures and the cost of obtaining the exposures. An illustration of the computation of these types of performance measures is presented below. Included in that illustration is a discussion of how we constructed measurements of document exposure time for the Free Library of Philadelphia.

It may be argued that these statements of library objectives, as encompassing as they are, do not cover all library benefits. In particular, it may be argued that the facilities provided by libraries are used, and are intended by the library to be used, in endeavors other than exposure to documents obtained through the library. For example, a university library may be used for study or reading of one's own materials, for socializing, and for classes. Also, a public library may be used as a general community meeting place for functions unrelated to document exposure.

However, in this paper we propose measures of performance based solely on document exposure. The exclusion of the tangential benefits that result from the existence of library facilities is partly a matter of expediency. Also, this exclusion is partly based on the notion that when the library is performing these additional services, it is not acting in its capacity as a library, which is to serve the social function of bringing together individuals and recorded experience.

Although the performance measure of document exposure is not a perfect measure, it includes the substantial portion of benefits due to library activity. If a library director feels that efficient maximization of document exposure is a too-limited conceptualization of his library's objectives, he may allocate part of the costs of facilities to the additional benefits. The allocation may be accomplished by sampling users to determine the extent of use of library facilities for purposes unrelated to exposure to documents obtained through the library. The remaining cost of facilities then may be associated solely with document exposure.

We are currently working on other variants of measures of performance based on document exposures, and, of course, alternative measures may be used by management at any particular time. Hence, for example in the private sector, management might use the ratios of profit to capital, profit to sales, and the dollar value of net profit as measures of the overall performance of a firm. Similarly, it might use measures such as ratios of current assets to current liabilities and inventories to sales for evaluation of particular aspects of a company's operations. Clearly, certain measures are more valid or useful for some purposes than others.

Library activity consists of two rather distinct aspects: (1) a passive or reactive aspect of satisfying demands by users for library materials and information, and (2) an active aspect of promoting library materials to create demands and to influence them. The reactive aspect may consist of almost all activity for certain types of libraries where users are highly educated individuals motivated toward library use and know what they want

—for instance, medical or legal libraries. Although the active aspect has very little importance in professional libraries, and some importance in college and university libraries, it is quite significant in public libraries (particularly in disadvantaged areas), as evidenced by its emphasis in the recorded public library objectives presented earlier in this paper.

The concept of document exposure includes both aspects. If a library improves its ability to satisfy demands by users, document exposure increases. Satisfactions result immediately in exposure and satisfied users tend to return for future exposure, while unsatisfied demand is lost and disappointed users often do not return. Likewise, if a library creates demands that otherwise would not exist, document exposure increases.

For libraries that emphasize reaction to users, and attribute very little importance to promotion of library use, then there are two simple performance measures which adequately reflect overall library performance. They are: (1) the proportion of user demands satisfied [2, 3]; and (2) the average time it takes to get the document or information to the user [4, 5]. However, for other libraries, where the active aspect is important, we propose document exposure measures. We suggest below three methods for measuring document exposure: exposure counts, item use-days, and exposure time.

The first method is to count each circulation (and each renewal), each direct in-library use, each interlibrary loan, and each indirect exposure as one unit of exposure. All exposures may be added together or separate counts may be kept for each exposure type. This method is easily accomplished for recorded exposures, such as circulations, interlibrary loans, and certain types of indirect exposures. For unrecorded exposures of in-library use and for some indirect exposures, these counts are more difficult. However, sampling methods may be used to estimate the number of direct and indirect in-library exposures per attendance. In this manner, attendance estimates may be converted into estimates of direct and indirect in-library exposures.

There are some disadvantages to this method of counting exposures. If separate counts are kept by exposure type, we have a multidimensional measure of output of library activity. Especially for the construction of library models, and for many evaluation purposes, this situation is awkward. For instance, it does not lead to an output per unit input nor to an output less input measure. Also, a separate measure for each exposure type would be difficult to construct because of the necessity of allocating inputs among exposure types.

If, on the other hand, we add all exposures together, we may be adding essentially dissimilar things. For instance, five charges from a reserve desk of a particular book, each charge having a time limit of one hour, results in five exposures. If the same book is circulated for four weeks, and is used for much more than five hours, there is only one exposure. A fast informational request is also one exposure. In addition, browsing exposures to ten different documents in an hour are not necessarily more beneficial than an hour of in-depth exposure to one document. One problem with a performance measure based on counting exposures and aggregating them is that a library could improve its performance merely by making its loan period very short. Whereas use for a particular period of time could have been accomplished with one circulation, the library could necessitate several renewals, several exposures, for use during that same period of time.

An alternative method for obtaining a single measure of output, without merely adding exposures, has been suggested by Meier [6]. It entails counting "item use-days." This measure differs from that of counting exposures because a long circulation involving exposure during X different days is counted as X item use-days, rather than as one exposure.

This method has the advantage of using a common unit of measurement across exposure types. Aggregation is accomplished by estimates of item use-days. In this way, it overcomes some of the difficulties inherent in the exposure count measure. This accomplishment is made at the expense of only one additional estimate—the average number of days of use per circulation or interlibrary loan. No additional estimation is necessary for direct or indirect in-library use. Each of these exposures in-

volves only one day, and is counted as one item use-day.

The estimate of the average number of days of use per circulation may be obtained by questioning the user, upon return, about the number of days he or anyone else had spent with a circulated document. If two or more persons use a circulated document on a given day, an equivalent number of item use-days is assigned to that day and document. By questioning users of similar libraries that differ in loan period, a curve of the type indicated in figure 2 would be expected.

Some of the arbitrary qualities inherent in the exposure count measure are present also in the item use-day measure. For example, five exposures of one hour each by an individual to a document on five different days are not necessarily better than a single five-hour exposure on one day. In the former case, there are five item use-days, compared with only one in the latter case. Also, browsing exposures to ten different documents in an hour result in ten item use-days, whereas an hour of in-depth exposure to one document results in only one item use-day.

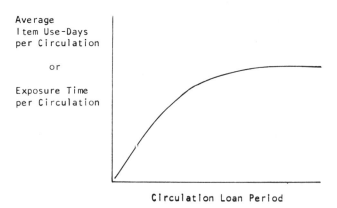

FIG. 2.—Average item use-day per circulation as a function of circulation loan period

A third measure, which eliminates the difficulties of the other two and creates some new ones, is to focus upon the amount of time an individual is exposed to a document. The common units for aggregation are estimates of exposure time. For recorded exposures, such as circulations and informational requests, it is necessary to estimate the average amount of time for each exposure type. This estimate may be obtained in a similar manner to that of item use-days—by questioning users returning a circulated document about time spent with it. Although individual recall may not be very accurate, in the aggregate, the estimated average time per circulation would probably be quite reliable. A curve similar to that for item use-days would be expected. Estimates of document exposure time for informational requests may be made by library staff members.

For in-library exposure time, there is no need to count exposures. An estimate of the average time an individual spends in the library could be obtained by monitoring arrivals and departures. The other necessary element is to estimate the percentage of the time in the library that users are in direct exposure to library materials or receive indirect document exposure from the library staff— as opposed to searching for library materials, talking with others, using bathroom facilities, etc. The estimates probably are quite stable over time for each library.

MATCHING EXPOSURE AND COSTS

An essential part of any performance measure is a periodic matching of the outputs (benefits) and inputs (costs) of an organization. A basic corporate accounting practice is the periodic matching, usually annually, of revenue and expense to determine net profit or loss.

However, in libraries, as well as in most nonprofit organizations, the only periodic matching is of cash receipts and disbursements. Usually, there is neither an attempt to measure library output nor to estimate the true costs of library operations. Therefore, it is impossible to match outputs and costs in order to evaluate library performance.

As indicated earlier, possible measures of the outputs of library activity include exposures, item use-days, or exposure time. Library performance evaluation can only be accomplished by matching with the exposures occurring in any period of time, the costs of facilities, equipment, resources, staff, and contracted services necessary to produce this exposure. Proper timing is a major problem because costs in a given year are not necessarily designed to produce exposure in that year. Present exposure often is a result of past expenditures, and present costs are often designed, in part if not completely, to produce future exposure. This fact is self-evident for all outlays acknowledged to be capital expenditures. However, it is also true that purchase and processing expenditures for library materials (documents) are designed to produce exposure in future years, in addition to the year of the initial expenditure. Even staff expenditures for certain library promotion programs may be investments in future exposure.

Corporate accounting practice recognizes that it is necessary for evaluation purposes to resolve timing problems inherent in all businesses. Libraries have analogous problems. Although separate records are generally kept for cash flows, the accrual basis of accounting is widely accepted. Revenue, the dollar measure of output of business operations, is recognized in the period when goods are sold or services performed, and expenses are recorded for appropriate time periods, irrespective of actual collection or payment in cash. In this manner, revenues and expenses are recognized in the year to which they relate, and the annual matching of revenues and expenses results in a more meaningful income determination.

Other essential aspects of the accrual method are charges for depreciation and adjustments for prepayments. No discussion will be given here of various possible depreciation and prepayment amortization methods. It suffices to note that in library accounting, because there is generally no periodic matching of output and input and no attempt to measure true costs for particular time periods, depreciation and prepayment methods are usually considered inappropriate. However, the important point for our present discussion is that it is essential for evaluating library performance to allocate capital expenditures and prepayments of all types over time.

Various accounting problems arise in attempting to match exposures and costs to appropriate time periods. However, these problems can be resolved on reasonable and consistent bases. For example, suppose a university library invests in documents which it is anticipated will be used by members of a planned but as yet nonexistent department. In this case, for purposes of constructing performance measures, the depreciation on the investment may be deferred until the department is formed and the document exposures take place.

ILLUSTRATIVE COMPUTATION AND USE
OF OVERALL ANNUAL PERFORMANCE
MEASURES

The concepts of exposure and the accrual method of matching expenditures with their output may be used to construct performance measures. Generally, there are two standard types of performance measures: (1) a ratio of benefits to costs, and (2) the difference between benefits and costs. The ratio performance measure is used particularly to evaluate most governmental operations when it is difficult to attribute a monetary value to benefits. For libraries, it would be exposure (counts, item use-days, or hours) per dollar.

The difference measure is analogous to profit in the private sector. It may be used for libraries if we can impute a monetary value for each unit of exposure. Then, the performance measure would be the difference between the imputed monetary value to society of exposure and the costs used to produce the exposure. This measure may be more meaningful in per capita form.

Let us illustrate the computation of overall, annual ratio and difference performance measures for the Free Library of Philadelphia for its fiscal year July 1, 1969–June 30, 1970. In this case, we define benefits in terms of exposure hours during the fiscal year, and costs in terms of all expenditures which produce the exposure hours included in the benefits. Let E = the number of exposure hours in the fiscal year by individuals to library documents obtained from the Free Library, V = the imputed monetary value to society of one exposure hour, C = total costs in the fiscal year including current expenditures designed to produce current exposure and allocated past expenditures, and N = the population of potential users. The library benefits may be described in terms of E, exposure hours; E/N, exposure hours per capita; VE, the imputed value of exposure hours; or VE/N, the imputed value per capita. The ratio measure which relates exposures to cost is E/C, exposure hours per dollar. The difference measure is $VE - C$, which, in per capita form, is $(VE - C)/N = V(E/N) - C/N$.

Although the Free Library performs district services for libraries in counties surrounding Philadelphia and performs resource services in certain subject areas for the state, we will define E and C solely with respect to services performed primarily for residents of the city of Philadelphia. Therefore, N is an estimate of the number of potential users of these services. The Bureau of the Census advance report of 1970 population characteristics indicates that the total population of the city of Philadelphia is 1,948,609, including approximately 126,816 children under the age of four. Let us exclude these children on the grounds that most of them are too young to be considered potential users, thereby reducing the population to 1,821,793.

Most of the document exposure produced by the Free Library by means of services for Philadelphia residents are utilized by these residents. However, the library also permits nonresidents to utilize these services. In addition to residents, let us include in the population of potential users an estimate of the number of nonresident users in the fiscal year.

There were 565,576 persons registered during the year. A sample of 16,455 registrants indicated that 9.7 percent of the registrants are nonresidents. Therefore, $(0.097)(565,576) =$ 54,861 persons are registered nonresidents. A sample of nonresidents entering the library shows that 72.4 percent are registered: for each 10,000 registered nonresidents, there are an additional $(0.276)(10,000)/0.724 = 3,812$ nonresidents who are not registered. Therefore, in addition to the 54,861 registered nonresidents, there are (54,861) $(0.3812) = 20,913$ nonresident users who are not registered. Adding these 54,861 + 20,913 = 75,774 nonresidents to the 1,821,793 resident potential users, we get $N = 1,897,567$.

The total number of exposure hours E consists of both circulation and in-library use. There was an annual circulation of 5,259,543. A sample survey of 308 persons returning 951 items of library materials indicated that the average amount of time spent by the borrower or anyone else with a circulated document is 2.25 hours. Therefore, there were $(5,259,543)(2.25) =$ 11,833,972 exposure hours via circulation.

In order to ascertain the number of in-library exposure hours, the first step is to estimate annual library attendance. Three library units—Central, Northeast Regional, and Mercantile—compile attendance records by means of turnstile counts: the annual total was 1,556,568.

The attendance at the other forty-six library units (forty-four branches and two bookmobiles) was estimated by dividing circulation by the average number of circulations per visit. We sampled five library units in May 1971 chosen at random from each of five groups created by a cluster analysis with respect to circulation, bookstock, size of building, and educational level of the surrounding population. The total number of persons entering these branches during the sampling activity was 767 and there were 699 circulations, yielding 699/767 = 0.911 circulations per visit.

An analysis of several years of monthly attendance and circulation records at Central, Northeast Regional, and Mercantile yielded monthly indices of the number of circulations per visit. The monthly index for May is, by coincidence, 0.911—that is, the May number of circulations per visit is 91.1 percent of the annual average. Therefore, the best estimate of circulations per visit for the forty-six library units without attendance counts is: May sample circulations per visit/May index = 0.911/0.911 = 1.00. At these units, the annual circulation was 3,831,867. The estimate of attendance is: number of circulations/circulations per visit = 3,831,867/1.00 = 3,831,867. Adding this figure to the attendance of the three units having turnstile counts yields an annual Free Library attendance of 1,556,568 + 3,831,867 = 5,388,435. Some of these persons stayed only for a few minutes and others stayed for hours. Based on an analysis of questionnaires on which time was recorded, we estimate that the average stay was 25.5 minutes or 0.425 hour. Multiplying the annual attendance by the time in the library per visit, we see that (5,388,435)(0.425) = 2,290,272 user-hours were spent in the library. A sample of user in-library activity showed that at any given time, on the average, 58 percent of the persons in the library are engaged in direct or indirect document exposure and 42 percent are engaged in other activities. It follows that 58 percent of the in-library

user-hours are in-library document exposure hours: (2,290,272)(0.58) = 1,328,358 hours. Adding this number to the 11,833,972 circulation exposure hours yields $E = 11,833,972 + 1,328,358 = 13,162,330$ exposure hours. The performance measure expressed in terms of exposure hours per capita is: $E/N = 13,162,330/1,897,567 = 6.94$ exposure hours per person.

In the 1970 fiscal year, the Free Library's operating expense budget for city library services was $8,356,655. Those expenditures incurred to produce a significant amount of document exposure in future periods are to be allocated to these periods: $979,847 for library materials, $160,442 for furniture and equipment, and $149,001 for materials and services related to branches that have not yet opened. The remaining portion, $7,067,365, may be associated with the current year. A small part of these expenses was devoted to promotion activities which were designed to have a carryover effect into the next year. However, no allocation to next year is made because the amount is considered small and the carryover of promotion activities from the prior year to the current one approximately equals the carryover from this year to next year.

Library documents are estimated to have, on the average, a ten-year life. All expenses incurred in order to get library documents on the shelves are to be allocated over this approximate period. The expenditure of $979,847 to acquire these documents obviously is in this category. In addition, it is estimated that 15 percent of all library staff expenses and other expenses is devoted to selecting, acquiring, classifying, cataloging, and processing library materials. Therefore, 15 percent of $7,067,365

= $1,060,105 is included in the amount of current expenditures invested in document resources available for immediate use, bringing the total to $979,847 + $1,060,105 = $2,039,952. The remaining portion of the operating budget, $7,067,365 − $1,060,105 = $6,007,260, represents current expenditures devoted entirely to producing current document exposure—that is, maintenance of facilities, circulation, maintenance and weeding of documents, promotion of library use, planning and administration, and various forms of reference services.

For purposes of constructing performance measures, expenditures for library documents are entered into an asset account which is depreciated each year. The account may be initiated by sampling the documents in order to estimate the number of volumes currently owned by the library which were obtained at different accession dates. Alternatively, we analyzed annual additions and withdrawals of various types of documents for each library unit. We assumed: (1) half of each annual withdrawal was from the oldest accession period(s); and (2) the other half was distributed over all accession periods proportionally with respect to the number of documents in the accession period at the time of the withdrawal. We began with 1953 balances of library documents and simulated annual additions and withdrawals through time. The results were estimates, for each library unit and type of library material, of the number of volumes currently owned by the library which were obtained annually from 1954 to 1970 or before 1954.

The current average purchase prices for library documents are shown in table 1. In order to determine the current unit values of recently acquired library documents, we must add to the purchase price an estimate of expenses per document for selecting, acquiring, classifying, cataloging, and processing. We have estimated that $1,060,105 had been devoted to these document services. Let us assume that each book category has the same cost per document for these services, and that the expenses for other documents (predominantly uncataloged pamphlets) are 20 percent of those for books. In the fiscal year, the number of book equivalents are: 27,696 Central adult books + 8,014 Northeast adult books + 61,027 branch adult books + 57,271 juvenile books + 59,424 (20 percent of 297,121) other documents = 213,432 book equivalents. The cost per book to be added to the purchase price is $1,060,105/ 213,432 = $4.97. For other documents,

TABLE 1

CURRENT COSTS PER UNIT OF NEW LIBRARY MATERIALS

	Purchase Price ($)	Additional Costs ($)	Total Costs ($)
Central adult books	6.86	4.97	11.83
Northeast adult books	5.76	4.97	10.73
Branch adult books	4.64	4.97	9.61
Juvenile books	3.01	4.97	7.98
Other documents*	0.62	0.99	1.61

* Uncataloged pamphlets; bound documents; broadsides; clay tablets; embossed volumes; films; horn books; large type books; manuscripts; maps; microfiche; microfilms; microcards; boxes of music; photos, pictures, and prints; sheet music; slides; sound recordings; talking books; tapes; unbound documents; and wood blocks.

the increment is 20 percent of $4.97 = $0.99. In table 1, we add these costs to the purchase price.

In order to estimate the current value of library materials on hand, we must take into account the fact that there is a sharp decrease in value over time because of obsolescence of content and deterioration of the physical document. We assume that the value per document to the library decreases exponentially over time.[2]

Finally, we obtain the current value of library materials on hand by multiplying the number of documents by the corresponding unit value. Summation over accession periods and document types yields the total value of documents on hand, $15,118,845.

A certain amount of this asset is depreciated each year to include part of document resource expenses in the current matching of exposure and expenses. Document use has been found to decrease exponentially with time due to obsolescence of content, deterioration of the physical document, and because the longer the document is held, the higher the probability of theft, loss, or misplacement. Therefore, we choose the declining balance method of depreciation in which a constant rate of depreciation is applied to a declining balance. We choose an annual rate of 15 percent, which results in approximately 80 percent cumulative depreciation after ten years. The depreciation for the 1970 fiscal year is 15 percent of $15,118,845

---

[2] If t = number of years since accession, assuming that the average pre-1954 document is twenty-five years old, we multiplied the current unit value by $_e{-}At$, where A was set to yield a unit value of $1.00 for pre-1954 branch adult books on hand: $A = 0.091$. There was librarian agreement that unit values obtained in this manner reflected the amount of current funds the library would be willing to spend to retain a typical document in its collection.

= $2,267,827. The document resource balance for the beginning of next year is $15,118,845 − $2,267,827 = $12,851,018.

Thus far, C, total costs for the 1970 fiscal year, consists of $6,007,260 of current expenditures devoted entirely to producing current document exposure and $2,267,827 of depreciation of library document resources. The final elements of C are depreciation of buildings, equipment, and furnishings. Straight-line depreciation is used over a fifty-year life for buildings (2 percent per year) and over a fifteen-year life for equipment and furnishings (6.67 percent per year).

The Free Library consists of forty-eight buildings which are currently providing city library services: the main library, Central; a regional library, Northeast; two special libraries, Mercantile and the Library for Blind; and forty-four branch libraries. We have compiled or estimated cost data on constructions, additions, renovations, and renewals. Expenditures made more than fifty years ago are considered completely depreciated. Depreciation for the 1970 fiscal period consists of 2 percent of all construction costs, site purchase costs, and related planning and architectural expenses not considered completely depreciated. These expenditures total $12,595,100 (construction costs) + $5,027,300 (addition, renewal, or renovation costs) = $17,622,400; 1970 depreciation is (0.02)($17,622,400) = $352,448.

Expenditures for equipment and furnishings are part of both the operating and capital budgets. In the past fifteen years, approximately $791,000 has been allocated for this purpose from the operating budget and approximately $649,000 from the capital budget, a total of $1,440,000. The fifteen-year, straight-line depreciation is $1,440,000/15 = $96,000 (table 2).

TABLE 2

TOTAL COSTS FOR 1970

Current expenditures devoted entirely to current document exposure	$6,007,260
Library document resource depreciation	2,267,827
Building depreciation	352,448
Equipment and furnishings depreciation	96,000
Total	$8,723,535

Pertinent data elements are: $C/E = 8,723,535/13,162,330 = \$0.66$ per exposure hour and $C/N = 8,723,535/1,897,567 = \$4.60$ per person, where $C = \$8,723,535$, $E = 13,162,330$ exposure hours, and $N = 1,897,567$ persons. The performance measure expressed in terms of exposure hours per dollar is: $E/C = 13,162,330/8,723,535 = 1.51$ exposure hours per dollar.

As expressed previously, exposure hours enhance individual knowledge, ability, creativity, motivation, and confidence. These educational outputs in turn further progress toward the fulfillment of the objectives of society. Therefore, exposure hours have a value to society. This value may be expressed in monetary terms: $V =$ the imputed monetary value to society of one exposure hour.

Inherent in the governmental decision to invest in library services is a decision to forego alternative governmental investments, and such nongovernmental uses of funds as private investment and consumption. The benefits of a governmental investment are expected to exceed costs to the extent that the resources utilized would result in benefits which exceed costs in the private sector [7, pp. 202–12].

Since funds can be invested in the private sector with an average rate of return of 10–15 percent, governmental benefits are expected to exceed costs by this rate [8, pp. 187–201]. If we assume that these expectations have been fulfilled by the governmental investment in the Free Library, we may estimate the dollar value imputed to an exposure hour.

Let us assume that the benefit-cost ratio is 1.10. Free Library benefits are VE and costs are C. Therefore: $VE/C = 1.10$, $V = 1.10/(E/C) = 1.10/1.51 = \$0.72$ per exposure hour. That is, it follows from the decision to invest in library services that each exposure hour produced by the Free Library has a monetary value of $0.72. Hence: $VE = (VE/C)(C) = (1.10)(\$8,723,535) = \$9,595,889$, $VE/N = \$9,595,889/1,897,567 = \$5.06$ per person, $VE - C = \$9,595,889 - \$8,723,535 = \$872,354$, $(VE - C)/N = \$872,354/1,897,567 = VE/N - C/N = \$5.06 - \$4.60 = \$0.46$ per person. Of course, the difference performance measure of $0.46 per person is what we expect because of the assumption of benefits exceeding costs by 10 percent (10 percent of $4.60 = $0.46). However, if V calculations were to be made for many libraries and averaged, we would obviate the necessity of making a specific benefit-cost ratio assumption in each case to obtain a value for V.

Computation of these overall library measures over time would enable library managers to trace major trends in performance. It would highlight the effect of major programs, such as the opening of a new branch. It would also focus attention on the effect of changes in the environment, such as the increasing use of individual book purchases in place of library use.

The overall performance measure may also be useful in comparison with other similar libraries. Major differences in performance may aid in specifying particularly effective programs.

The illustrative computation of the performance measure was in terms of the entire library. However, perhaps the most important use of library performance is in terms of evaluating individual library programs or aiding in library decisions. A similar computation may relate exposure and costs associated with a program. A program may be any identifiable subset of library activity, such as special services for part of the population of potential users, promotion of certain specific documents, a particular library function, an individual library unit, or any combination of these. A program may be evaluated by predicting its effect on exposure and costs over time. In this context, allocation decisions must be made in order to identify the specific exposure, costs, and population associated with the program. Analysis of past effects of programs on benefits and costs may be useful in predicting future effects.

In order to evaluate programs which have an effect over more than one year, we define: E_t = exposure in year t (where $t = 0$ for current year, $t = 1$ for next year, etc.) attributed to a given program, C_t = cost in year t attributed to a given program, and r = the interest rate applicable to government projects. Receipts (or payments) of X dollars, or something having a value of X dollars, today, next year, and t years from now, are not the same things. The sooner money, or something having a monetary value, is

received, the sooner it can be put to work to earn money. The later money is to be paid, fewer current dollars need be set aside to ensure the payment. In fact, P_0 dollars (or dollar value) today is equivalent to $P_0(1 + r)$ next year, and to $P_t = P_0(1 + r)^t$ in t years. Therefore, in order to convert dollars or dollar value received or paid in year t to dollars received or paid today, we must divide by $(1 + r)^t$. The result is the discounted present value of future receipts or payments.

As stated previously, exposure has an imputed monetary value. Therefore, predicted exposure over time must be discounted. The discounted present value of exposure attributed to a given program is

$$\sum_t \left[\frac{V}{(1+r)^t} \right] E_t = V \sum_t \frac{E_t}{(1+r)^t}.$$

Similarly, the discounted present cost attributed to a given program is

$$\sum_t \frac{C_t}{(1+r)^t}.$$

The difference measure is:

$$\sum_t \frac{VE_t}{(1+r)^t} - \sum_t \frac{C_t}{(1+r)^t} = \sum_t \frac{VE_t - C_t}{(1+r)^t}.$$

The ratio measure is:

$$\frac{V \sum_t (E_t)/(1+r)^t}{\sum_t (C_t)/(1+r)^t},$$

In the ratio measure, the V value may be eliminated. Programs with the highest expected discounted benefits less costs or benefits per unit cost may be adopted.

In a similar manner, the effect of specific library decisions on exposure and costs may be analyzed in order to aid library managers in making these decisions. Mathematical models are particularly useful in tracing the impact of various decision alternatives upon the performance of the organization and to select the one alternative that yields the best performance.

The models identify important variables or alternatives subject to the control of the decision maker and other important variables or events which are not subject to his control. These variables are related to each other and to their joint effect on the performance measure. The manager then is able to ask "what if" type questions and evaluate them with respect to their effect on library performance.

An example is a set of models we have developed which predicts the change in document exposure and costs for any given change in the proportion of titles duplicated. The first step was to estimate the average amount of time a book is off the shelf (the effective loan period) by using the annual circulation and the proportion of books on loan at a given time. We then constructed a queuing model which predicts demand as a function of circulation, the effective loan period, the number of books in the subject-area collection, and the proportion of these books which have never circulated. We used estimates of demand to construct a regression model which relates demand for books in a subject area with the number of graduate students in courses and the number of faculty with interests relating to the subject area. Analysis of circulation rates for books of various publication dates enabled us to allocate the pre-dicted demand over subcollections, defined in terms of publication date in addition to subject area. Finally, we have developed a model which utilizes the subcollection demand prediction and the effective loan period to predict the extent of document exposure for any given proportion of titles duplicated in the subcollection. The library decision maker may analyze changes in exposure and costs for any given extent of duplication. In this manner, he may compare library investment in duplicate copies with library investment in other areas, and determine the best duplication proportions for each subcollection.

Another example is a model we have constructed for public libraries. It predicts the extent and distribution of exposure for each area of a city, for any given allocation of funds between document resources and service effort, between adult and juvenile services, and among library units. Other important variables considered in the model are the educational level of users and potential users of library units and the quality of the physical facilities.

LIBRARY STANDARDS

Thus far, we have analyzed what a library tries to accomplish (its objectives), and we have proposed library performance measures to evaluate how well the library is achieving these objectives. It is revealing to take a brief look at library standards against this background. Standards are neither objectives nor performance measures. Objectives are general statements of purpose and performance measures are a quantitative means of relating benefits (outputs) to costs (inputs). Library standards are either descriptive rules for "proper" management or are quantitative rules for "minimum" inputs of materials, personnel, and physical facilities. However, they are often considered to be objectives or performance measures, or both.

The most up-to-date presentation of public library standards is the American Library Association's *Minimum Standards for Public Library Systems, 1966* [9]. The preface states: "[This document] presents minimum standards; that is, it describes the least the citizen living in the last third of the twentieth century has the right to expect." There are sixty-six general guiding principles, organized in sections of Structure and Government of Library Service, Service, Materials—Selection, Organization, and Control; Personnel; and Physical Facilities. For each guiding principle, there are one or more standards. An example of a standard that is a descriptive rule for proper management is: "22i. To ensure quality service all sources of information and all forms of materials must be consulted." An example of a standard that is a quantitative rule for "minimum" input is "39i. . . . At least one currently published periodical title should be available for each 250 people in the service area." Unit and total cost estimates for meeting these "minimum standards," for populations of different sizes, are discussed in Plain [10].

Descriptive rules are useful to the extent that they provide reasonable advice to library administrators. The purpose of most quantitative standards is "to prod or scare most communities into raising budgets in the belief that improvement would be generated" [11, p. 2]. These standards are useful to the extent that they increase library receipts, resulting in an increase of library inputs of materials, personnel, and physical facilities, in turn resulting in greater document exposure.

Most university library standards have been either descriptive in nature or based upon value judgments. In contrast, the recently published data for fifty of the better university libraries in the United States and Canada by the Committee on University Library Standards [12, 13] are in terms of average, range, and quantiles. However, the major emphasis is still directed toward measuring inputs to the library, as opposed to measuring outputs or benefits imparted to the users. The one exception is in the area of reserve and circulation service, wherein data are presented on a per library basis as well as a per student basis. Further, the defining of input measures in the areas of expenditures, document resources, personnel, and space on a per student basis represents a significant improvement in the development of input indicators (for example, volumes per student). Development of comparable measures relating to the research function of the university would represent a further significant advancement in the area of input indicators.

Unfortunately, the standards are not very helpful in evaluating the effectiveness of any particular library. They merely serve as a guide for comparing gross input data in the areas of expenditures, space, personnel and document resources, and circulation data of a particular library with gross input and circulation data for fifty of the better university libraries.

Both university and public library standards fail to provide a basis for meaningful evaluation of the performance of the library for the following reasons: (1) most of the standards are descriptive in nature, making evaluation extremely difficult; (2) most of the standards which prescribe quantitative objectives are arbitrarily formulated by value judgments; (3) the emphasis of the standards is directed toward evaluating the input resources of the library, as opposed to evaluating the difference between the output, (exposure benefits imparted in the user-library interface) and the input; and (4) the standards discourage experimentation with different programs and different allocations of input resources designed to meet the needs of the library's particular population of potential users; merely meeting the standards implies, perhaps falsely, that the library is doing an adequate job.

A library performance measure is a yardstick to determine how well a library is performing, analogous to a measure such as return on investment in the private sector. If a measure were to be generally adopted, distributions of the measure could be established for libraries of similar types. These distributions could be used to establish certain performance levels as performance standards.

SUGGESTIONS FOR FUTURE RESEARCH

A few suggestions are given below concerning future research which seems to be desirable, and implications of operations research and management techniques for educational programs for librarians.

In the area of performance measures, further research is clearly required in the construction of other types of measures as well as of the types of indexes presented here, the testing of their feasibility, and the determination of their advantages, disadvantages, and general usefulness. Although the performance measures discussed in this paper possess the capability of incorporating weighting factors for the importance of different types of document exposures, of different population groups, etc., more work needs to be done on how such weights could be assessed and whether their inclusion would result in more useful performance indexes than the unweighted ones. It would be particularly helpful for managerial purposes to learn what factors affect a performance measure and to what extent. For example, in university libraries, how are the numbers of document exposures (for example, in reserve and general circulation) affected by undergraduate and graduate enrollments, research activity, and other factors? Information of this sort would be very useful for staffing, book purchasing, and other decisions. We have done some work in this area, but much more is needed.

Since only a very small part of the library managerial process has been discussed here, much of the remainder remains to be researched. Once the objectives of the library are determined, the program structures required to carry out these objectives must be specified. Research is needed on the defining of program structures, the identification of program outputs, the variables under the control of decision makers which generate the outputs, and the environmental constraints which operate as limiting factors. Further development of analytical models for library planning and decision making is needed. In the context of this paper, research is needed which relates factors under the control of decision makers to library performance measures, that is, to program outputs and costs.

Some other research suggestions are perhaps best posed as questions. The first is an extremely broad query. What is the best strategy for implementing modern management techniques in libraries? More narrowly, how should library managerial-decision models developed by us and other investigators be tested for possible implementation and use? To what extent should a library attempt to develop its own expertise in an area such as systems analysis? What is the proper mix of development of in-house capability and the use of outside consultants? How do the answers vary by type and size of library? What is the appropriate mix of library professional, nonprofessional, and technical personnel? How much library effort should be devoted to operations-research activities?

What is the best way to educate and train librarians in managerial techniques which have actual or potential usefulness? How can the library profession develop knowledgeable, inventive, and imaginative people who will depart from the bias of present patterns and who will create new and better patterns, institutional frameworks, and technical advances? Furthermore, how can the profession carry out this development while simultaneously promoting the traditional humanistic and service values it has always cherished?

On the matter of the implications of fields such as operations research and systems analysis for the education of librarians, almost any suggestions run the risk of being both presumptuous and simplistic. The period of formal professional education of librarians is far too brief to include work in depth in such technical areas competing for places in library curricula as systems analysis, information theory, operations research, management information systems, managerial accounting, and organization theory. The library profession has been responding to the felt need for work in these areas with formal and informal educational programs including special courses, clinics, conferences, training programs, new journals, and other means. Clearly, it is neither feasible nor desirable for all librarians to become specialists in these fields. In the way of teachers, we leave with a question. What is the best combination of formal and informal education for librarians to develop understanding of the various methodologies, to develop abilities to communicate effectively with technical personnel, to recognize areas for fruitful applications of fields such as operations research, to evaluate critically recommendations for technological and methodological applications, and to develop the type of creative and imaginative librarians alluded to earlier?

REFERENCES

1. "Statement of Service to Library Users." *ACRL News* 27 (April 1966): 21–22.
2. Morse, Philip M. *Library Effectiveness: A Systems Approach.* Cambridge, Mass.: M.I.T. Press, 1968.
3. Buckland, M. K.; Hindle, A.; Mackenzie, A. G.; and Woodburn, I. *System Analysis of a University Library.* Lancaster: University of Lancaster Library, 1970.
4. Orr, R. H.; Pings, V. M.; Pizer, I. H.; and Olson, E. E. "Development of Methodologic Tools for Planning and Manag-

ing Library Services. I. Project Goals and Approach." *Bulletin of the Medical Library Association* 56 (July 1968): 235–40.

5. Orr, R. H.; Pings, V. M.; Olson, E. E.; and Pizer, I. H. "Development of Methodologic Tools for Planning and Managing Library Service. II. Measuring a Library's Capability for Providing Documents." *Bulletin of the Medical Library Association* 56 (July 1968): 241–67.

6. Meier, R. L. "Efficiency Criteria for the Operation of Large Libraries." *Library Quarterly* 31 (July 1961): 215–34.

7. Baumol, William J. "On the Appropriate Discount Rate for Evaluation of Public Projects." In *Program Budgeting and Benefit-Cost Analysis*, edited by Harley J. Hinrichs and Graeme M. Taylor. Pacific Palisades, Calif.: Goodyear Publishing Co., 1969.

8. Stockfish, Jacob A. "The Interest Rate Applicable to Government Investment Projects." In *Program Budgeting and Benefit-Cost Analysis*, edited by Harley J. Hinrichs and Graeme M. Taylor.

Pacific Palisades, Calif.: Goodyear Publishing Co., 1969.

9. American Library Association. *Minimum Standards for Public Library Systems*. Chicago: American Library Association, 1966.

10. Plain, E. "Costs of Public Library Service 1968." *ALA Public Library Association, Just between Ourselves*, vol. 7, no. 3 (October 1968).

11. Beasley, Kenneth E. "A Theoretical Framework for Public Library Measurement." In *Research Methods in Librarianship: Measurement and Evaluation*, edited by Herbert Goldhor. Evanston: University of Illinois, Graduate School of Library Science, 1968.

12. Downs, Robert B. *University Library Statistics*. Washington, D.C.: Association of Research Libraries, 1969.

13. Downs, Robert B., and Heussman, John W. "Standards for University Libraries." *College and Research Libraries* 31 (January 1970): 28–35.

ADDITIONAL BIBLIOGRAPHY

American Library Association. *Library Statistics: A Handbook of Concepts, Definitions, and Terminology*. Chicago: American Library Association, 1966.

Beasley, Kenneth E. *A Statistical Reporting System for Local Public Libraries*. University Park: Pennsylvania State University, 1964.

Bowler, Roberta, ed. *Local Public Library Administration*. Chicago: International City Managers Association, 1964.

Brutcher, E.; Gessfor, G.; and Renford, E. "Cost Accounting for The Library." *Library Resources and Technical Services* 8 (1964): 413–31.

Buckland, M., and Woodburn, I. *An Analytical Approach to Duplication and Availability*. University of Lancaster Library Occasional Papers, no. 2. Lancaster: University of Lancaster, 1968.

Buckland, M., and Woodburn, I. *Some Implications for Library Management of Scattering and Obsolescence*. University of Lancaster Library Occasional Papers, no. 1. Lancaster: University of Lancaster, 1968.

Burkhalter, Barton R., ed. *Case Studies in*

Systems Analysis in a University Library. Metuchen, N.J.: Scarecrow Press, 1968.

Clapp, Verner, and Jordan, Robert. "Quantitative Criteria for Adequacy of Academic Library Collections." *College and Research Libraries* 26 (September 1965): 371–80.

Fussler, H., and Simon, J. *Patterns in the Use of Books in Large Research Libraries*. Chicago: University of Chicago Library, 1961.

Hayes, Robert M., and Becker, Joseph. *Handbook of Data Processing for Libraries*. New York: Becker & Hayes, 1970.

Houser, Lloyd J. "Effectiveness of Public Library Services: Development of Indices of Effectiveness and Their Relationship to Financial Support." Ph.D. thesis, Rutgers University, 1967. ERIC no. ED 024 405. ERIC reports are available from: Leasco Information Products, Inc., 4827 Rugby Ave., Bethesda, Maryland 20014.

Jain, A. K. "Sampling and Data Collection Methods for a Book-Use Study." *Library Quarterly* 39 (July 1969): 245–52.

Jain, A. K.; Leimkuhler, F. F.; and Anderson, V. L. "A Statistical Model of Book Use and Its Application to the Book Storage Problem." *Journal of the American Statistical Association* 64 (December 1969): 1211–24.

Jain, A. K. "A Statistical Study of Book Use." Ph.D. thesis, Purdue University, 1968.

Leimkuhler, Ferdinand F. "Mathematical Models for Library Systems Analysis." *Drexel Library Quarterly* 4 (July 1968): 185–96.

McGrath, William E., and Durand, Norma. "Classifying Courses in the University Catalog." *College and Research Libraries* 30 (September 1969): 533–39.

McGrath W.; Huntsinger, R.; and Barber, G. "An Allocation Formula Derived from Factor Analysis of Academic Departments." *College and Research Libraries* 30 (January 1969): 51–62.

Martin, Lowell. *Baltimore Reaches Out: Library Service to the Disadvantaged.* Deiches Fund Studies for Public Library Service, no. 3. Baltimore: Enoch Pratt Free Library, 1967.

Martin, Lowell A. *Library Response to Urban Change: A Study of the Chicago Public Library.* Chicago: American Library Association, 1969.

Orr, R. H.; Pings, V. M.; Olson, E. E.; and Pizer, I. H. "Development of Methodologic Tools for Planning and Managing Library Services. III. Standardized Inventories of Library Services." *Bulletin of the Medical Library Association* 56 (October 1968): 380–403.

Raffel, Jeffrey A., and Shishko, Robert. *Systematic Analysis of University Libraries: An Application of Cost-Benefit Analysis to the M.I.T. Libraries.* Cambridge, Mass.: M.I.T. Press, 1969.

Roy, R. H., et al. *Operations Research and Systems Engineering Study of a University Library Progress Report.* Baltimore: Johns Hopkins University, 1963.

Roy, R. H., et al. *Operations Research and Systems Engineering Study of a University Library Progress Report.* Baltimore: Johns Hopkins University, 1965.

Salverson, Carol A. "The Relevance of Statistics to Library Evaluation." *College and Research Libraries* 30 (July 1969): 352–61.

University of the State of New York. State Education Department. Division of Evaluation. *Emerging Library Systems: The 1963–66 Evaluation of the New York State Public Library System.* Albany: University of the State of New York, February 1967.

Wheeler, J., and Goldhor, H. *Practical Administration of Public Libraries.* New York: Harper & Row, 1962.

Williams, G.; Bryant, E. C.; Wiederkehr, R. R. V.; Palmour, V. E.; and Siebler, C. J. "Library Cost Models: Owning versus Borrowing Serial Publications." ERIC no. ED 026 106, 1968.

CATALOG USE IN A LARGE RESEARCH LIBRARY

BEN-AMI LIPETZ

ABSTRACT

Concern with the questions of when and how best to computerize the catalog of a large research library, and how to improve an existing conventional catalog, motivated a study of the utilization of the main catalog of the Yale University Library. The study was carefully designed to provide a representative sample of catalog use. Traffic through the catalog area was observed over a period of more than a year. A schedule of interviews with catalog users was based on observed traffic volume by hour of day, day of week, and time of year. More than 2,000 interviews were completed, using nonleading interviewing technique. Information was derived on the catalog user's objective, starting clues, and university affiliation. Search success was determined. Follow-up studies were performed on the catalog cards and the actual books identified in successful searches. Reasons for search failure were determined for known-item searches. Availability and accuracy of different categories of search clues were ascertained. Published algorithms for searching computerized bibliographic files were evaluated. Attention was given to the feasibility of automatic construction of computerized catalogs. Some of the available results are presented and discussed.

INTRODUCTION: GENERAL OBJECTIVES

This paper summarizes a study of catalog use that was carried out at the main library of Yale University. The study was carefully designed to produce valid information on a variety of topics related to catalog use, including volume of catalog use, nature of the user population, types of catalog searches attempted, responsiveness of the catalog, and potential responsiveness of the catalog.

The primary motivation for this study was a twofold conviction: First, that computerization of the catalogs of all or most large libraries is inevitable sooner or later. Second, that knowledge to guide library managers in determining when the time for conversion has arrived and how it should properly be accomplished is lacking. A secondary motivation, of course, was interest in the immediate possibility of improving the conventional card catalog while it remains in use.

The foregoing statements about computerization of catalogs should not be construed as indicating that library catalogs have never been computerized. Indeed, some have—but not the catalogs of the very large research libraries that we are concerned with here. To the multimillion-book library, the automation projects that have been carried out on the catalogs of smallish collections are only interesting and suggestive experiments, not mandates to emulate.

On the other side of the issue, there are some obvious and powerful arguments to keep the large libraries from plunging into catalog computerization right away. One is the high cost of equipment—the gigantic fast computer memory required for storage of the text already in the large card catalogs has barely been developed yet and would be prohibitively expensive for libraries. Then, too, there is the huge cost of retrospective conversion of existing

129

catalogs to machine-readable form. Optimistically, these two problems will be resolved: the first by technological advances that will lower the cost of computers and related equipment; the second through sharing of data conversion efforts by means of standardization and distribution projects such as MARC.

But even when computerization of the large library catalog becomes technically and economically possible, there will still be the valid problem of determining how to design the computerized catalog to do its job most efficiently. Merely trying to put into a computer all of the features of a conventional card catalog would tend to preserve any drawbacks that are inherent in the physical nature of conventional catalogs and would tend to overlook possible improvements.

To solve this design problem rationally, one must know what library users really want from catalogs. But available knowledge on this matter of catalog use is woefully inadequate. The study reported here was undertaken to help fill the void.

Catalog-use studies are not a novelty. Quite a large number (mostly projects for masters' degrees) have been reported in the literature. But all of the older studies seemed to have flaws in their design which made their reported results suspect or unusable. Very commonly they were based on exceedingly small samples of catalog users, casting grave suspicion on any findings. Often they were based on highly incomplete returns of questionnaires, raising the question of whether nonrespondents constituted a set of users systematically ignored by the findings. In many studies, use of questionnaires distributed to catalog users some time after a catalog search raises doubts regarding the reliability of human recall of the details of their search activity. And in studies using questionnaires or interviews there was frequently evidence or the strong possibility of questions being asked in such a way as to bias the results. The present study was designed to avoid all of these methodological weaknesses.

The study was conducted over a three-year period ending in late 1970. It was supported by a grant from the U.S. Office of Education. An extensive report on the work has been published [1], and the results reported here are largely a selection from that report. Credit is due to Frederick G. Kilgour for the original suggestion of the need for a research study of this kind and to Peter Stangl, who was primarily responsible for the implementation of the research design and the preliminary reduction of data.

SPECIFIC OBJECTIVES: DESIGN OF THE STUDY

The study was concerned specifically with utilization of the public card catalog of the Yale University Library. This catalog is located in the main hall of the Sterling Memorial Library building. It is a single-alphabet catalog, containing some 7 million cards in some 7,000 drawers. It contains full sets of catalog cards for the more than 3 million volumes housed in Sterling Memorial Library, and at least main-entry cards for the more than 2 million volumes housed in the other sixty or so libraries of Yale University. (Catalogs in the branch libraries contain full sets of cards for their respective holdings.) The main catalog is open to the public. The stacks of Sterling Memorial Library are open to Yale students and faculty and to many authorized outside users. The catalog area is a scene of constant activity, with people entering to make searches of various kinds and durations, then leaving with different degrees of satisfaction and edification.

Basically, every catalog search is a word-matching exercise in which the user attempts to match some known clue (for example, a name, or a title, or a subject term) against the filing terms in the catalog—in the hope of finding some useful associated information on the catalog card, such as a call number or a complete bibliographic description of a work. The success or failure of a catalog search depends on several factors: whether or not the desired material is in the library to start with; the clues which the catalog user brings to a search; how he applies them; and the file terms and associated data provided in the catalog. The study was designed to cast light on all of these factors.

A crucial consideration was the establishment of a clearly representative sample of catalog searches to study. There are several hundred thousand searches made every year, roughly 1,000 each day. Sampling was essential in order to hold study costs and annoyance of catalog users to reasonable levels. The desired representative sample was obtained by making very careful observations of traffic in the catalog area, then purely on the basis of observed traffic selecting a sample of specific searches to study. The observation of traffic consisted of counting the number of people entering the catalog area (through several entries) during various hours of the day, portions of the hour, and days of the week, for more than a year. (Actually, several other kinds of traffic statistics

were obtained at the same time; all of these traffic measurements contribute to understanding of demand patterns for catalog facilities.) After the first ten weeks of observation, a profile of catalog-use rates was constructed; using this, an interview schedule was constructed that would yield approximately a 1 percent sample of catalog searches, completely representative of the observed traffic profile. Interviews with catalog users were carried out for a full year using this schedule. Throughout this period, observations of catalog traffic were continued in order to check on the consistency of the original observations and to provide a basis for appropriate weighting of interview results for periods in which any significant change in traffic pattern was observed.

Interviews were conducted by several staff members, each with a rigid, predetermined schedule to follow. The interviewer was required to be at a particular entrance to the catalog area at a specified time and on a specified day, and was to interview the first person to enter and begin to use the catalog within a specified number of minutes. The purpose of the interview was to learn as much as possible about the objective of the search about to be performed and the clues available to the catalog user. Interviewers were carefully trained to avoid leading questions; they used a standard set of questions which started off deliberately vague ("What were you about to do here at the catalog when I interrupted you?") and became more specific only if full details were not elicited with the vague questions. Information was sought on the type of search to be performed, on the motivation for the search, on the clues which the catalog user had in his mind (spellings were requested of author names and uncommon terms), on the clues which the catalog user had available in written notes or printed matter (these were photocopied), on his intended search approach, on the nature and length of his association with Yale University, and on the frequency of his use of the library system. The refusal rate among catalog users who were approached for interviews was less than 1 percent; most interviewees were delighted to be asked about their searches. The average interview took only a few minutes to complete. In all, more than 2,100 interviews were completed during the study year.

After an interview, the user was permitted to complete the catalog search but was kept in view from a distance until leaving the catalog area. He was then approached a second time and asked whether his search had been successful, what call numbers he had identified to satisfy his requirement, and how many terms he had looked up during his search. If he was uncertain about the success of the search but was going elsewhere in the library to continue it (for example, to the stacks to look over some possibly useful books), he was given a simple follow-up form on which to report results afterward.

A third type of data gathered in this study (in addition to catalog traffic observations and interviews with catalog users) was on matching and potential matching of users' search clues to catalog filing terms. In the case of successful searches, call numbers of desired books were obtained from the catalog users. With these numbers it was possible later to obtain photocopies of the corresponding catalog

cards from the shelf-list file. It was also possible to borrow the actual books at a later date and to photocopy those portions of the front matter and back matter which could potentially be used for creating catalog-file terms under a highly formalized, possibly automated, cataloging procedure; candidate portions of the book included title pages, contents, preface, and indexes. These photocopied cards and book pages were appended to the respective interview records for purposes of comparison.

Partial analysis of the data amassed in this study was accomplished through the use of computers and statistical techniques. The traffic observations were easily transcribed on punched cards for machine analysis. Interview and follow-up data were more difficult to transcribe; too much detail was available about users and catalog cards and books. However, by inventing abbreviated codes and formats, it was possible to record on punched cards whether or not a given category of data was available from an interview and, if so, the range of values or alternatives in which it fell. It should be understood that the selection of categories of data to record in this manner is largely subjective; there is ample possibility for further analysis of the collected data. In this study, about forty variables were identified.

By computer, the co-occurrence of each variable with each other variable was calculated. From the results, it was possible to identify pairs of variables that are linked to each other in some way that is probably no coincidence. For these pairs of variables, detailed matrixes were printed out for more careful scrutiny. These matrixes included tables of actual data values, row percentages, and column percentages.

For some of the questions investigated in this study, purely manual data analysis methods were used.

RESULTS

Traffic observations permitted the plotting of a number of graphs showing the pattern of demand on catalog facilities. For example, figure 1 shows how catalog use varies from hour to hour during the day (in half-hour intervals); it can be used in assigning librarians to the catalog area to provide a consistent level of reference service throughout the day.

Variations in catalog use from week to week throughout the year are plotted in figure 2 in terms of both users per week and users per hour of library open time. (Open hours are usually reduced during recess periods and holidays.) The graphs clearly indicate the difference in activity level between the academic year and the summer vacation period. Also indicated is the tendency for catalog use to drop below normal at the beginning of a holiday or recess and then rise above normal at the end of that interval.

Superimposed on the graph of catalog users per week in figure 2 is the plot of books per week circulated from Sterling Memorial Library over the same period of time. The two curves match almost perfectly, indicating that a measurement of the profile of either parameter can be used by librarians for predicting the other parameter. It is not suggested that every use of the catalog results in the borrowing of exactly one book; that degree of match

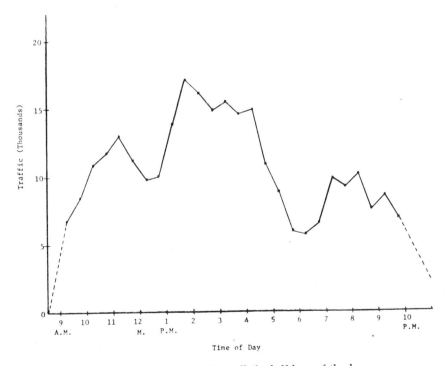

Fig. 1.—Yearly weekday catalog traffic by half-hour of the day

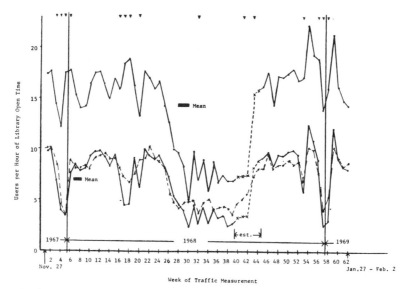

FIG. 2.—Weekly catalog traffic and weekly book circulation. ▼ = weeks with shortened library hours; --- = users in week in thousands; —— = circulation per week in thousands.

in figure 2 is probably coincidental. Many books are selected for borrowing by shelf browsing without using the catalog. Many catalog searches result in failure, or in the selection of more than one book. Still, in aggregate, all of these possibilities tend to add up throughout the entire year to a consistent pattern in which catalog use and book borrowing are always in the same proportion.

Throughout the week, there is variation in catalog use from day to day (table 1). Monday, Tuesday, and

Wednesday traffic is above average; the other days, below. There is a steady decline in traffic after the peak on Tuesday.

Interview data yielded valuable information on the nature of the catalog-user population and on the relative activity of different user groups throughout the year (table 2). Graduate students are the heaviest users. Their relative use of the catalog remains constant through the year (although absolute use of the catalog drops to half in the summer period). Undergraduates are the next heaviest users; their use is concentrated in the academic year and is lower for freshmen than for other undergraduates in terms of the number of potential users. Faculty and staff show up as comparatively light users of the catalog (but this does not necessarily indicate their comparative level of use of books in the library). About one-fifth of catalog use throughout the year is by persons not actively affiliated with the

TABLE 1

VARIATION IN CATALOG ATTENDANCE
BY DAY OF WEEK

Day	Entrants per Hour	Percent of Yearly Average
Monday	100.4	104.7
Tuesday	106.5	111.1
Wednesday	102.0	106.4
Thursday	95.0	99.1
Friday	92.6	96.6
Saturday	81.7	85.2
Sunday	82.5	86.0
Yearly average	95.9	100.0

TABLE 2

ACADEMIC STATUS OF CATALOG USERS BY SEASON

STATUS	APPROXIMATE ELIGIBLE POPULATION	CATALOG USE (%)		
		Full Year	Academic Year	Summer
Yale freshmen	1,600	7.0	8.3	12.3
Other Yale undergraduates	2,900	24.9	27.7	
Graduate, postgraduate students	4,700	35.5	35.6	34.9
Yale faculty	5,000	8.8	7.3	16.0
Yale staff		3.3	2.9	5.0
Non-Yale students	?	9.5	9.9	7.6
Non-Yale faculty	?	3.2	2.8	5.3
Yale faculty family	5,000	1.5	1.1	3.3
Visitors, retirees, others	?	6.3	4.3	15.7
Total	...	100.0	99.9	100.1

university; this use is relatively much greater during the summer period.

Determination of the distribution of catalog-search objectives was among the most interesting results of the study (table 3). Four general search

TABLE 3

DISTRIBUTION OF SEARCH OBJECTIVES

Search Type	Immediate	Underlying (%)
Document	73	56
Subject	16	33
Author	6	6
Bibliographic	5	5
Total	100	100

objectives were identified. The objective of a "document search" is to determine whether and where the library holds a work that the user already knows to exist. This is the most prevalent type of search. A "subject search" is for pertinent works on a known topic. An "author search" is to determine what works if any are available from some known author or publishing body; selection of specific works may or may not follow from this determination. A "bibliographic search," like a document search, is for a known work, but the objective is to make use

of data from the catalog card and not to locate or borrow the book.

In terms of immediate intent at the time of interview, almost three-fourths of the catalog users are interested in document searches. However, when these users were asked at the end of their interviews about what they would do in the case of an unsuccessful search, a very substantial number stated that there were other ways to get the needed information. This indicated clearly that the underlying objective was to find information on a particular topic (that is, to perform a subject search), and that looking up a known book on the subject was only an expedient approach. In terms of underlying motivation, about one-third of catalog searches are subject searches, but half of these are sublimated to document searches in using the existing library catalog.

The rate of success in document searches was 84 percent (table 4), and about the same in other types of searches. Success rates did not vary much among different groups of users. Evidence of a library frustration factor among newcomers to Yale (which would be indicated by decreasing use of the catalog throughout the year

TABLE 4

SUCCESS AND FAILURE OF ATTEMPTED DOCUMENT
SEARCHES

Result of Search	%
Document in catalog, located by user	84
Document in catalog, not located by user but found by research staff through user's starting clues	5
Document definitely or probably exists but was not in catalog at time of user's search	10*
Document possibly in catalog, user's clues inadequate or grossly inaccurate	1
Total	100

* One-fifth of this group of documents were added to the catalog from one to twelve months after the user's unsuccessful search.

studied) could not be found. There was evidence that undergraduates occasionally try to use search clues that are not necessarily filed in the catalog (for example, title of an analytic, name of a translator, title of a publisher's series) but tend to abandon them after a year or two.

The reasons for failure of document searches were determined by having the project staff repeat the searches at a later time, using the clues available at the time of the original search. Also, standard bibliographic tools were employed to help verify the existence of the desired works. Of the sixteen (of 100) searches that ended in failure, ten failed because the desired books were not in the collection at the time of the search (but two were added soon afterward). Another five searches should not have failed; the user did not use all of the clues available to him or did not use them correctly. In one search out of 100 it was impossible to determine whether the failure was user fault, catalog deficiency, or absence of the desired work. There is apparently far more to be gained from increasing collection size and improving catalog

users' orientation than there is from attempting to increase the complexity of the existing catalog. Indeed, it is conceivable that reinvesting the savings from somewhat reduced cataloging effort could actually increase search success rates. However, this conclusion could be negated if evidence is adduced to suggest that increased complexity would attract many new users or uses.

In a document search, the intended approach (table 5) is usually through

TABLE 5

INTENDED APPROACH TO DOCUMENT SEARCHES

Approach	%
Author name (personal or corporate)	62.0
Title of monograph or periodical	28.5
Subject term	4.5
Editor name	4.0
Author or title of portion of work (analytic)	0.5
Series title	0.2
Other (publisher, translator, geographic location, etc.)	0.3
Total	100.0

the author of the desired work. (This makes particularly good sense in the catalog studied, since the author approach is the only one provided for many of the works represented in the catalog.) A sampling of the records of actual successful searches (table 6) shows that two or more look-ups are required in about 15 percent of the searches because of errors in either clues or approaches. The availability and accuracy of author clues and title clues are compared in table 7; there is very little basis for favoring one approach over the other when both are available. The availability and accuracy of catalog users' knowledge of publishing date are shown in table 8;

TABLE 6

INTENDED AND ACTUAL APPROACHES FOR 126 SUCCESSFUL KNOWN-ITEM SEARCHES

Approach Intended	Item Found Under	Number of Look-Ups Required				
		1	2	3	4	5
Author	Author	73	5	...	...	1
Author	Title	...	1	...	...	...
Author	Added title	...	1	...	...	...
Title	Title	23	3	2	1	...
Title	Author	...	...	1	...	...
Title	Added author	...	1	...	...	...
Added author	Added author	4	1	...	...	...
Added title	Added title	2	...	...	...	...
Subject	Subject	5	1	1	...	...
Total	...	107	13	4	1	1

TABLE 7

AUTHOR AND TITLE DATA IN DOCUMENT SEARCHES
(%)

Result of Search	Author Data	Title Data	Title Data × 82%
1. Applicability to desired documents	82	100	82
2. Availability in search clues (right or wrong). Sum of 3–7	77	97	79.5
3. Available, complete, and accurate in search clues ...	42.3	61.5	50.4
4. Available in search clues, but only partially complete and accurate (last name, first corporate level, or first title word correct and in place)	23.2	15.0	12.3
5. Available in search clues, inaccurate	10.5	15.5	12.7
6. Available and accurate in search clues, appears in catalog card but not designated as a file entry	0.7	1.6	1.3
7. Available in search clues but not on catalog card, accuracy not determined	0.3	3.4	2.8

NOTE.—Third column percentages normalized to facilitate comparison of title data with author data since the latter apply to only 82% of document searches.

date of publication would clearly not be a productive primary approach of the catalog.

The availability of both users' author and title clues and the correct bibliographic data (from the actual

TABLE 8

AVAILABILITY AND ACCURACY OF PUBLICATION DATE INFORMATION IN DOCUMENT SEARCHES

Result of Search	%
"No information" on date	41
Information more than five years wrong	12
Information two to five years wrong	18
Information one year wrong	10
Correct year	19

books or their catalog cards) made it possible to evaluate, by manual simulation, two published algorithms [2, 3, pp. 133–36] for effecting computer retrieval from author-title files despite inaccurate clues. One algorithm uses word compression before matching; the other uses word truncation before matching. Results of these evaluations were published previously [4, 5, pp. 125–27]. Both algorithms yielded 70 percent computer retrieval in a test group of 126 searches which had been 100 percent successful by the manual approach.

It is unlikely that any single computer algorithm will match human performance in manual-file searches. However, it does seem likely that using a combination of algorithms could give much better retrieval than a single algorithm. Combining the two algorithms that were tested, for example, would raise the success rate to about 75 percent. However, each algorithm retrieves false drops along with valid references, and the number of false retrievals increases with file size and with the number of algorithms employed. The key to effective suppression of false retrievals is in the use of exclusion criteria along with selection criteria (for example, "published after 1945 and before 1960," or "must deal with biology"). Although the temptation is strong to strip computerized bibliographic files down to the categories of author, title, and call number in the interest of economy, there is good reason to believe that a file so stripped cannot possibly give adequate retrieval performance.

The possibility of automatic construction of adequate computerized catalogs was considered through examination of front and back matter in retrieved works and comparison of this material with user clues. The examination hypothesized use of a machine that would transcribe specified portions of

a book into machine-readable form followed by identification and alphabetization of nontrivial terms. It seems possible that a catalog adequate for document searches could be constructed by this method, even if little or no human interpretation of the data were incorporated. For subject searches, however, a very large amount of human intervention and interpretation seems indispensable until such time as computers are able to cope with synonyms and distinguish key portions of text from trivia.

CONCLUSION

This study provided, at best, only a few pieces of the answer to the original question of when and how to computerize a large library catalog and to the secondary question of how to improve a conventional card catalog. However, it is a start. It should be remembered that the results reported here pertain specifically to the catalog at Yale and are not necessarily applicable to other libraries. Other recent studies [6, 7] have shown general agreement with these findings; but more research is needed. The data collected for this study have been only partially analyzed so far. Further results will be reported as they become available.

REFERENCES

1. Lipetz, Ben-Ami. *User Requirements in Identifying Desired Works in a Large Library.* New Haven, Conn.: Yale University Library, 1970.

2. Ruecking, Frederick H., Jr. "Bibliographic Retrieval from Bibliographic Input: The Hypothesis and Construction of a Test." *Journal of Library Automation* 1, no. 4 (December 1968): 227–38.

3. Kilgour, Frederick G. "Retrieval of Single Entries from a Computerized Catalog File." In *American Society for Information Science, Proceedings.* Vol. 5, *Annual Meeting, October 20–24, 1968, Columbus, Ohio.* Westport, Conn.: Greenwood Press, 1969.

4. Lipetz, Ben-Ami; Stangl, Peter; and Taylor, Kathryn F. "Performance of Ruecking's Word-compression Method When Applied

to Machine Retrieval from a Library Catalog." *Journal of Library Automation* 2 (December 1969): 266–71.

5. Stangl, Peter; Lipetz, Ben-Ami; and Taylor, Kathryn F. "Performance of Kilgour's Truncation Algorithm When Applied to Bibliographic Retrieval from a Library Catalog." In *American Society for Information Science, Proceedings.* Vol. 6, *Annual Meeting, October 1–4, 1969, San Francisco.* Westport, Conn.: Greenwood Press, 1970.

6. Tagliacozzo, Renata; Rosenberg, Lawrence; and Kochen, Manfred. *Access and Recognition: From User's Data to Catalog Entries.* Communication no. 257. Ann Arbor: University of Michigan, Mental Health Research Institute, 1970.

7. Palmer, Richard P. "User Requirements of a University Library Card Catalog." Doctoral thesis, University of Michigan, 1970.

IMPLICATIONS FOR LIBRARY EDUCATION

ABRAHAM BOOKSTEIN

ABSTRACT

Education in the use of quantitative methods is likely to become an increasingly important part of a librarian's education. In such an education, the development of appropriate attitudes may be more important than mastering particular techniques. This paper examines the nature of decision making in libraries, with the view of learning what qualities ought to be developed while in a library school. The discussion is illustrated by means of a simple model analyzing the problem of congestion at a catalog. The importance of library experience in making such an analysis is stressed. The concluding section of the paper raises questions that the author feels must be answered before operations research (O. R.) can be successfully integrated into a library school curriculum.

INTRODUCTION

The previous authors have given us a clear idea of the wide scope of operations research (O. R.), and in particular of its application to library problems. Their papers ranged from the theoretical to the practical; from the speculative to the down-to-earth. I would now like to review some of its aspects from the point of view of the library school. In doing this, I shall be describing skills and attitudes that are prerequisite to an O. R. investigation and presenting some thoughts as to how such skills might be developed in the course of a library school education. My approach, however, suggests that the impact of O. R. on library schools will extend beyond the introduction of courses on library management.

This approach will be quite general in that I shall be emphasizing the nature of O. R, as an intellectual framework rather than as a kit of techniques. For our purposes, O. R. is a way of looking at the world—other speakers used the phrase "state of mind"—and of approaching situations requiring decisions. In this sense, its techniques are not thought of as constituting its whole, but rather as being a consequence of its methodology as applied to problems of management. This is sometimes forgotten because of the great emphasis given to mathematical models in an O. R. curriculum. The originators of this field did not have most of these specialized models available for their use. They were people with scientific training, asked to use their skills to solve socially urgent problems. Much of their work involved rather simple mathematics, the sophisticated mathematics associated with O. R. today being developed to a large extent as a result of these investigations. When we talk of O. R. here, we will be referring to the attitudes of these founders rather than the subsequently developed techniques. The ideal of an O. R. program in a library school, then, would be to develop an ability in library students to create O. R. techniques anew—an O. R. adapted to library problems.

The approach of O. R. has much in common with the scientific method:[1]

[1] A classical description of the scientific method may be found in [1]; [2] presents a balancing

it requires a precise, often abstract, formulation of the essential features of a problem, a willingness to undertake methodical investigation to produce the information needed for decision making, and the analytic ability to recognize the consequences of this information. The ability to respond to a problematic situation in this manner should be an asset for any librarian, regardless of his formal rank, who will be in a position to influence decision making. The same kind of skills may be needed to plan and develop a large information network or to modify the operations of a single department of a library. In the following I shall, for brevity, use the term "manager" to refer to all such people.

This paper will be subjective, since, for a topic as broad and as new as O. R. is for librarianship, it is not possible to foresee every implication or authoritatively to set down guidelines to be followed; in a sense, such an approach is antithetical to the philosophy of O. R. itself. Rather, I will discuss some aspects that seem to me to be likely to prove consequential for library education and state some of the difficulties I believe the introduction of such an approach into a library curriculum will entail.

In a paper of this kind there is the serious danger of seeming to overemphasize one aspect of a very broad and complex topic as if others did not exist. Education for librarianship—as is true for education in general today—is in a great state of flux. The introduction of quantitative techniques is but one of many innovations in the library school curriculum. Certainly considerations of the library in relation to society, of its methods and its history, must continue to have a prominent position in a librarian's education if he is to consider himself truly a professional. I will not be discussing these issues here, but it is not with the intention of denying their importance.

NATURE OF TRAINING FOR O. R.

Traditional library education has often emphasized instruction in a body of practices; a student in such a program learns to handle a canonical set of events in a manner found effective in the course of library experience. Such training, if accompanied by an understanding of the principles and reasons for library practice, is essential, and must certainly continue as part of a librarian's education. However, a person who will be responsible for managing a large library must also learn to deal with very complex situations in which creative decision making is required. Generally such decisions are of a nonrecurrent nature and must be arrived at in the face of insufficient information or considerable uncertainty. This aspect of education involves not so much the transmission of knowledge that has been properly certified, as teaching the student to think analytically and critically and sharpening his ability to make difficult judgments. Such instruction forms an essential part of an O. R. education.

Intuition and experience are too often used to excuse a lack of analysis when it comes to justifying a managerial decision. The methods of O. R. make the decision-making process a much more taxing enterprise; far from dispensing with intuition and experience, it brings

view. Both would have some validity for the topic of this conference. A brief discussion of the application of scientific methodology to organizational problems can be found in most O. R. textbooks (e.g., [3]).

these-traits to a focus on the problem at hand. In a sense, the effect of O. R. is not to make management decision making easier, but more difficult.

The first step of an O. R. approach is the creation of a model that reflects those aspects of the situation essential for arriving at a correct decision. The appropriateness of this model is critical to the ensuing process; it will influence the collection of data; it will largely determine the decision ultimately to be reached. If the model is inappropriate, if it somehow misses the point, it is likely to lead to solutions of problems unrelated to those of concern to the manager—and possibly at considerable expense as well. There are many ways of getting poor results more simply and economically than through O. R. If used judiciously, however, O. R. can be very valuable in providing insights that allow a manager to use his wisdom most effectively; a good manager is always starved for the information that would confuse a less-talented worker.

These considerations might best be illustrated by means of a simple example. A question that has recurred in library literature is that of congestion at the card catalog [4]. This question often arises in polemics as to whether or not a divided catalog is superior to a dictionary catalog. One can argue that the use of subject heading cards tends to take more time than that of author-title cards, since the user is uncertain as to which item he is looking for and must therefore examine a number of cards, taking time to consider each one. The conclusion that follows is that congestion could be reduced if only these subject heading cards could be segregated in their own catalog. On the other hand, as Lubetsky [5] shrewdly observed, dividing the

catalog might "relieve congestion at the author-title catalog, but at the same time seriously aggravate congestion at the subject catalog, where all the subjects will now be compacted in a smaller number of drawers than they occupied in a single catalog." Clearly some balance must be sought, and to the extent that congestion is an important consideration it would be useful to be able to estimate ahead of time the effect of changing the form of the catalog. The approach of O. R. to this problem is to abstract from the extremely complex problem of catalog use those facets of importance to the problem of congestion. If the library manager is able to do this *without overlooking some important but perhaps subtle property of catalog use,* he can use analytic techniques to estimate the effect of changing the form of the catalog. But note the importance of the emphasized qualification: The correctness of this estimate depends on the model having a reasonable resemblance to reality. Here the judgment of the manager is crucial; it is he, not an expert consultant he may call in, who is ultimately responsible for judging the validity of the model. He must deeply understand the structure of the catalog and behavior of the patrons regarding it. He must see the subtleties that a consultant inexperienced with libraries might overlook. But he must also understand that an O. R. model *is* an abstraction from reality, and that many properties of the catalog will not be represented; it is precisely this simplification that makes the model subject to analytical treatment. Here again managerial judgment is called for: the manager must decide whether or not the process of abstraction is so severe as to limit the value of the model; but he must balance this with the consideration that the model at its best is no more than an approximation of reality—this is why we used the word "estimate" rather than "prediction" to describe the results of this process.

In my own treatment of this problem [6] I studied the contribution to congestion of each drawer of the catalog, considering both the arrival of users at the drawer and the time required for a use as occurring randomly and independently. I assumed that the distribution of time required for subject-card use could differ from that of author-title card use, but that for the purpose of the model, the distribution was the same regardless of whether the subject cards were isolated or mixed with author-title cards.

In this model, the scenario at a drawer of a dictionary catalog is then as follows: A user arrives at random times; a biased coin is flipped to determine whether he intends to use subject cards or author-title cards; if the catalog drawer is being used, he gets in line and waits until it is free; if or when it is free, he occupies the drawer for an amount of time determined by the appropriate probability distribution. For the divided catalog a similar process occurs at each of two drawers from the subject and author-title components, though here the biased coin is flipped to determine which drawer the patron will choose rather than which type of card he uses within a single drawer.

The model has a number of advantages. It is simple and capable of analytical treatment, a consideration not to be lightly dismissed. Indeed, once the essential features have been abstracted, the model resembles one that occurs very often in O. R. literature, and once this similarity is recognized, one is able to take advantage of a considerable amount of research already completed. This feature is not unusual for O. R. studies and is one of the strengths of this approach. For it appears that a great many outwardly disparate situations can be reduced to relatively few models, which means that it is not necessary to approach each situation anew; one can cumulate research on a few useful models. In a similar manner, once the analysis of a card catalog is completed, one can draw immediate conclusions about book catalogs.

The model also makes more precise the nature of the problem. The single term "congestion" really represents three related but different phenomena: it might denote the problem of there being too many people in the area of the catalog; it could mean that there is an intolerably high probability that a desired drawer will be found already in use; or it might mean that an intolerably long wait is necessary, on the average, before one can use a drawer. These three criteria for congestion demand different treatment and can lead to different conclusions. An analytical approach can often crystallize in this manner a number of aspects of a problem; this is valuable for arriving at a reasonable solution to the problem as well as for the deeper intellectual insights it offers.

We finally note that the model advises the manager as to what data are required before a conclusion can be reached. It is sometimes overlooked that blind data gathering is expensive and of limited value. The results of our model take the form of a number of formulas, and it is the parameters in these formulas that constitute the data that the manager must acquire.

If the above model has its advantages, there are also a number of reasonable questions that can be raised concerning it. Should one take into account that splitting the catalog will require a larger number of cards because of card duplications? To what extent is the behavior of a person using a drawer influenced by the knowledge that someone else is waiting for it? Should the model reflect instances where users intend to look up more than a single author or subject, and thus can go to another drawer if one is busy? Does the behavior of different classes of users differ in this respect? Whether these effects are significant enough to invalidate the model is the legitimate concern of a manager who might have to make a decision on the basis of the analysis.

Further, managerial responsibility does not stop with an evaluation of the model—congestion is but one of a number of considerations involved in deciding whether a catalog should be split; the cost of creating and maintaining a split catalog and the possibility of user confusion are among the most important. The model, if it is a reasonable approximation to reality, can give the manager an estimate of the effect of congestion. This must then be balanced with the other considerations before a conclusion can be reached. To neglect these other considerations could be analogous, in the business world, to optimizing the operation of the stockroom at the cost of the collapse of the whole corporation.

The example just cited contains, at almost every step, implications for the library school. It makes quite clear the necessity of a library manager's having an extensive background in the intricacies of library operations; this experience cannot be assumed of a consultant only casually interested in li-

brary affairs. Whether the individual carrying the responsibility will, in the future, receive his primary education in business-oriented disciplines supplemented by library training or the reverse is not clear; this will be decided in part by the reception given by library schools to programs in management science. But in either case, the task of providing at least the training in librarianship that such a person will receive does reside with the library school if it is to be accomplished with reasonable efficiency. Both cases will involve the library school's developing close relations, and perhaps even joint programs, with departments teaching mathematics, statistics, and management science, as well as modifying its own programs to satisfy the expectations of its management-oriented students. Members of a library school faculty will have to be familiar with programs of these other departments so as to best guide students to courses of interest.

An important decision that will have to be made is how much technical training is to be required of a library manager and to what extent he should depend upon outside experts for technical guidance. This question becomes more difficult to answer if we recall that we mean by the term "manager" all library workers who might in some way be in a position to influence library operations, not only persons holding such a title explicitly. Wherever the balance is struck, as a minimum a library manager may be expected to be familiar with the basic philosophy of scientific inquiry and mathematical analysis. He should be sufficiently conversant in the language of mathematics that he will be able to understand the results of an O. R. analysis and to anticipate what might reasonably be accomplished—both its potentials and its limitations. He should certainly know what the basic models of O. R. are and be familiar with its terminology; this will permit intelligent communication with consultants should this be required. It has often been noted that the manager must play an important role in any O. R. project [3]. It is he who is ultimately responsible for the organization's functioning. He must make his goals clear to the O. R. experts; he must guide the analysis with respect to the subtleties of his organization; he must make sure that the conclusions and suggested implementations are acceptable. Otherwise he runs the danger, mentioned by Mr. Buckland, of conducting a study which results in an elegant and clever paper in an O. R. journal but which is worthless for the problem at hand. If the manager is easily overawed by the mathematics or jargon that play an important part of most O. R. analyses, it is not likely that he will be able to provide this guidance; he is likely to replace a badly operating system by a better-documented badly operating system, and perhaps have to pay for a computer to boot. (It is of course possible that the original system was functioning so badly that even a badly managed study of its operations could result in improvement, but this does not take advantage of the full power of O. R. methods.)

If the library school is responsible for introducing its students to the techniques of O. R., it has the more subtle but equally important task of developing their powers of judgment and critical thinking. A student must be able to see beyond the formulation of a model such as presented above; he must be able to ask pointed questions

and make judgments of validity. Though much of this maturity will develop only after he gains experience in the field, the process should begin at school, which is, in a sense, an institution for providing guided and accelerated experience. This experience could prove crucial in determining his ultimate success.

There are a number of ways of developing this kind of judgment. No doubt the intensive study of successful projects would be very valuable; probably an intensive study of badly designed projects will prove even more valuable. Another method that has met with some success in business education, but which to my knowledge has not been tried in library schools, is the use of computer games.[2] Computer games are a method for simulating real-life experiences in the classroom. A student is given such information as he might have available if he were working on an actual project, and he must make decisions on the basis of this information. A decision may be, for example, to investigate further in order to get still more information. The computer is programmed to simulate the real world as accurately as possible. It will provide the student with such additional information as he might reasonably ask for, complete with price tag. The program would be designed to include the effects of the environment of the library, such as the occurrence of uncertain events and decisions by other people, some of whom might also be playing the game. The game would incorporate such diverse elements as the price of books, the size of enrollment at a university, or the effect of urban renewal in the

[2] I have been informed by Mr. Buckland that such a game is being planned at the University of Lancaster. This is described in [7].

vicinity of the library, and so forth. While playing, the student would be able to compare conclusions drawn from his models with decisions of the computer, which painstakingly considers the effect of every known variable. Playing such a game could provide a very stimulating and instructive experience and might even be of value to a seasoned manager.

Thus far, in my discussion of O. R. and how it might best be incorporated into a library education I have emphasized the practical skills and attitudes required for conducting a project. But there is another aspect of O. R., in the broad sense that I am using the term, that may well have a greater impact on library education.

Before proceeding, it may be useful to make some distinctions within O. R. that are often made about science in general. Science has been divided roughly into applied and pure science, with the former sometimes being referred to as engineering or technology and representing those aspects of scientific knowledge that have been developed to satisfy a practical end. Though the engineer receives a scientific education, he is more a practitioner than a research scientist, at least in his capacity as an engineer. With a few notable exceptions, the scientific work done in industry is of the applied kind. Pure scientific work, on the other hand, is more often done in universities and in government laboratories. Though these are polar concepts, and a continuous spectrum of scientific activity may be found, this distinction can be of value.

I would like to suggest that a similar division can be made regarding O. R. We here distinguish the O. R. worker in the field, who wishes to utilize skills and knowledge already developed to make a specific organization function more effectively, from the researcher developing new techniques. Though they may, in some cases, be embodied in the same person, we consider them as acting in different capacities.

Until now my paper has concentrated on O. R. of the applied kind and the education needed for such work. It is to pure O. R. that we now turn our attention. As is the case with "pure science," we can think of pure O. R. as further divided into theoretical and experimental categories. Here again the line is not precise, but the distinction is nonetheless useful. Theoretical O. R. concerns itself with developing the properties of the abstract models used. Typical accomplishments of this work are proof that a particular kind of linear programming model will always have integer solutions, or that in some waiting-line problems there is a necessary increase in idle time if service is to improve. One might here concern oneself with developing more efficient algorithms or finding different kinds of random number generators for simulation programs. Such studies would typically be carried out in departments of applied mathematics or industrial engineering.

On the other hand, by experimental O. R. I mean the use of O. R. methodology for investigating the properties of particular types of systems, such as libraries. This category is meant to refer to work that is of general enough interest so as to transcend its value for any particular application, that is, the results of this effort, if made public, can be used by other workers, sparing them the effort of repeating the research. In this manner, as different workers contribute the results of their research, a body of knowledge builds up, producing the cumulative effect associated with the growth of science. Work in this area can require considerable skill in experimental design and statistical analysis. Here the results of even a well-planned project may be inconclusive; their main value may turn out to be the debate they engender, which in turn suggests further and more pointed investigation. The totality of this work may lead to a deeper understanding of the processes involved, which in turn may result in field techniques useful in applied work. This work should result, in the long run, in our libraries being managed more efficiently and providing better service for their patrons.

The nature of what we call "experimental O. R." as applied to libraries has at least two facets: determining precisely what the goal of an O. R. study ought to be, and discovering the relevant facts of library functioning. The former involves asking O. R. workers to contribute to the very sensitive and complex ongoing debate as to what are the goals of a library. Much of the discussion on this topic is vague and sometimes even confusing. Such ambiguity is inimical to an O. R. approach, which demands that objectives be expressed with mathematical precision. This demand is in a sense a weakness of O. R. in that an issue so complex and with so many nuances as library objectives may not lend itself readily to such precise description. I believe that the major weakness of O. R. work in libraries can be traced to precisely this inability to express management objectives with the precision needed for mathematical analysis. But is not this also a strength of O. R.? Does it not lend insight to library operations to attempt this kind of precision? In the simple model referred to earlier we noted the burden upon man-

agement of having to decide which of three measures of congestion is the one he is most interested in minimizing; but if this creates extra work for the manager, it also gives him further insights into the nature of traffic at the catalog. That he may not have been previously aware that the vague term "congestion" consists of three components does not mean that they did not previously exist, and it is difficult to see how their continued confusion could benefit management.

This line of reasoning extends to higher-level problems about libraries as well. Indeed, much of the difficulty in using O. R. for library problems represents not so much an inadequacy of O. R. as it reflects the complexity of library operation. It asks of library thinkers what exactly it is that they wish to accomplish, and suffers from their inability to respond. But it does make clear—perhaps uncomfortably clear—where more effort must be put. By forcing precise and explicit connections between general goals and actual operations to be made, O. R. will help clarify our basic understanding of libraries. In this way the results of experimental O. R. work will have an impact on the general philosophy of library science and will influence education even for traditional librarianship.

One can work toward these insights in different ways. The most obvious one is the intensive discussion, criticism, and improvement of previous efforts; one asks of each article: why is this not quite perfect? Another approach may be to reverse the standard pattern of O. R., which is to formulate the problem in the form of a model and then to analyze this model to get an optimal solution. It might well be more illuminating to ask what model is in fact being optimized by current practice. In the simplest cases, this will amount to manipulating parameters in, say, a linear programming model, though more sophisticated efforts can be imagined. The results of such an enterprise are likely to be surprising but may give some insight into what is in reality of interest to library planners today.

It may well be the case that just as our simple catalog congestion model made us aware of three different problems where previously only one was recognized, this approach, in a similar manner, will reveal distinctions in library goals. It might make much clearer the differences between public libraries, where much current thought on library practice centers on introducing groups with no tradition of reading to the library, and the university library, whose emphasis may be on facilitating access to documents for an already motivated community. In the latter case, money may be spent not so much to maximize circulation per dollar as to buy access to a vast variety of documents, the bulk of which may never be used. It is likely that a careful analysis will show that the university library itself may best be conceived of as a number of separate "libraries" sharing processes and physical surroundings but having different goals.

This discussion on clarifying library goals by means of O. R. really involves an additional use for O. R. models; that is, these models are not used as part of a problem-solving system but as a formal language for communication. Once we set up satisfactory models for library functions, we have made a great advance even if these models cannot, given the present state of the art, be solved. For to succeed at establishing these models will require a far better

understanding of libraries than we have today. Perhaps O. R. can play a role in problem formulation very similar to ALGOL (algorithm-oriented language) in algorithm description.

The other aspect of experimental O. R. referred to, that of getting additional information on a library's operation, is of course, closely related to that of clarifying its goals. Studies such as that of Ben-Ami Lipetz on catalog use address themselves to this need for more information. They provide useful information for managers and enhance our understanding of libraries. Very often, suggestions for such investigations will result from attempts to create models for libraries. Attempts to answer the questions raised regarding the catalog congestion model will involve such research.

We must now broach the sensitive issue of where and by whom studies of experimental O. R. on libraries should be conducted. It would seem that the library school would be the most appropriate institution for such research since it is here that expertise on libraries is concentrated. This would have the additional advantage that librarians are likely to learn more easily of such research than they would if it were conducted by people from other disciplines, and would be more influenced by this research as it would really be addressed to their problems. In this manner the research will acquire a greater sense of continuity, with librarians and researchers learning and profiting from each other's work, and its results will have a greater likelihood of implementation.

Another source of such research would be the larger libraries, but there are strong reasons why the emphasis should lie with the academic library school. In particular, research projects can be very expensive, and libraries are usually relatively poorly funded institutions. Here we must consider not only the cost of men and machines, but must also realize that much of true research is not successful, and more than one project must be funded for each significant advance. It is not very likely that a library manager will use much of his limited funds to finance research whose value to his library is uncertain or indirect and may be realized only in the distant future. Business firms that have significant research and development projects are generally quite large, and the projects will tend to be a small fraction of the total budget.

Generally, the source for high-risk research has been the university. In a sense the university institutionalizes the recognition of the social necessity of research whose practical value is not clearly established. For the researcher in a university maintains a dual role—that of researcher and teacher. The university, accepted by society primarily as an educational institution, does not have to justify its existence in terms of the consequences of the research of each faculty member. The sum of university research, however, has been of inestimable value to society.

Unfortunately, in the past the library has been unable to rely upon the university library school to generate the research it needs. This is partially because there are not as many library schools as, for example, physics departments, and also because library schools have generally considered themselves as professional rather than research-oriented institutions. In the past, library schools have not always been successful in attracting highly qualified, research-oriented people into their faculties, and often instructors are asked to carry a heavier teaching load than their colleagues in other departments. The results are predictable, if not cheering: Librarians have had to look to institutions outside the library school for much of the significant research relating to their professions.

The traditions of the library schools will make it difficult for them to be converted into research institutions—for tradition relates not only to a habit of mind among the faculty, but also to patterns of funding and the size and nature of the faculty. Nonetheless, to develop the body of knowledge required to meet the future needs of libraries, it will be necessary for the library school to overcome these barriers to research and to assume some of the characteristics of an academic department as well as those of a professional school.

CONCLUSION

I would like to conclude this paper by making some observations and noting some difficulties regarding the introduction of O. R. into a library school curriculum. Some of these have been referred to already.

1. Will the library school be able to attract faculty and students with a scientific background? This to a large extent will involve informing students of science of the interesting problems of a technical nature that do exist in libraries. The well-known tendency of people unfamiliar with library operation is to very greatly underestimate the practical and intellectual challenges offered by problems associated with large libraries. Should these challenges be communicated, it is likely that capable people will respond to them. It will also be necessary to make clear that librarianship, traditionally a humanistic discipline, does welcome indi-

viduals with technical backgrounds. Considering the recent growth of interest in libraries by O. R. workers, I believe that increasing numbers of people with technical backgrounds can be encouraged to involve themselves with library problems if they can be convinced that positions in libraries and library schools will be open to them.

2. How will the new faculty be incorporated into the school? A difficulty I see here is that library schools tend to be rather small, and not many schools will be able to introduce more than a single representative of the field into their faculty. However, scientific enterprise is increasingly being conducted by teams of workers. This problem will be alleviated, in part, if there are members of other faculties in the parent school who are interested in library problems. An associated problem for many library schools is that of reducing teaching loads to an extent that would permit time for research.

3. To what extent should all library students be required to learn O. R., and to what extent should this be considered an area of specialization? One might extend this question to ask how much O. R. should a specialist in library management learn and how much of this should be taught by the library school itself. It is certainly premature to attempt a definitive answer. I do think that it is possible to argue that all librarians could profit from some knowledge of research methods and of basic statistical technique. Such knowledge is not only of value for management; it will be an increasingly useful asset for all librarians whose work involves more than attending to clerical details. Library literature is sharing in the trend of the social sciences of becoming increasingly quantitative, and it is reason-

able to ask of a student that he be able to read intelligently the literature of his profession. If the library school can develop in its students an ability to evaluate such literature and to abstract what is sound from what is questionable, it will have fulfilled a good part of its obligations to the student and the profession. The amount of mathematics required for this would be considerably smaller than for a specialist in O. R. Certainly algebra and elementary statistics will be important, with the emphasis being put on math as a form of communication, supplementing speech in much the same way as diagrams do.

The techniques unique to O. R. may very well be restricted to a smaller group of students, though we note that many of its essential aspects require a relatively small mathematics background. One can very easily understand a formulation of a linear programming model without knowing all of the variants of the simplex method for solving the model. Furthermore, even within the domain of management, most problems will not require an extensive background in mathematics for their solution.

4. Will the introduction of quantitative methods increase the time required for a library education? Here little can be said at this stage. We merely note that the time required for obtaining a degree in sister disciplines, such as business administration, has had a tendency to increase as these fields become more quantitative.

The exact form of a program designed to introduce quantitative methods in the library school is still unclear, since this approach is very young in librarianship. It does seem, however, that interest in accomplishing this is spreading among library educators, and such programs are likely to become part of the education of increasing numbers of librarians.

REFERENCES

1. Cohen, Morris R., and Nagel, Ernest. *An Introduction to Logic and Scientific Method.* New York: Harcourt, Brace & Co., 1934.
2. Kuhn, Thomas S. *The Structure of Scientific Revolutions.* Chicago: University of Chicago Press, 1962.
3. Wagner, Harvey M. *Principles of Operations Research.* Englewood Cliffs, N.J.: Prentice Hall, Inc., 1969.
4. Heinritz, Fred. "Does Dividing the Catalog Relieve Congestion?" *Library Research and Technical Services* 8 (September 1964): 310.
5. Lubetsky, Seymour. "Crisis in the Catalog." *Catalogers' and Classifiers' Yearbook* 8 (1939): 48–54.
6. Bookstein, Abraham. "Queueing Theory and Congestion at the Library Catalog." To appear in the July 1972 *Library Quarterly.*
7. Mackenzie, A. Graham. *Library Association Record* 73 (May 1971): 90–92.

A SELECTIVE BIBLIOGRAPHY ON LIBRARY
OPERATIONS RESEARCH

VLADIMIR SLAMECKA

NOTE

Operations research may be interpreted in a broad sense as the use of the scientific method to solve management problems, or in a narrower sense as the application of mathematical programming techniques to management. In this bibliography, the broad interpretation is assumed.

In general, the literature items selected employ or discuss the scientific method as it is applied to problems of library management. The references are roughly grouped into four categories: General, Mathematical Programming, Modeling, and Systems Analysis. This bibliography excludes numerous documents which employ mathematical approaches *not* in the context of the scientific method, statistical studies, cost analysis of library operations, and literature concerned with operational problems of documentation. The bibliography covers approximately a fifteen-year period ending 1970.

The compilation of this bibliography was assited by Mr. T. C. Ponder, graduate research assistant in the School of Information and Computer Science, Georgia Institute of Technology, under grant GN-655 by the National Science Foundation.

GENERAL

Ackoff, R. L. "The Role of Recorded Information in the Decision Making Processes: Operational Research Approach." In *Documentation in Action*, edited by J. H. Shera, A. Kent, and J. W. Perry. New York: Reinhold Publishing Co., 1956.

Advanced Information Systems. "Activity Statistics for a Large Biomedical Library." Part 2 of the Final Report on the Organization of Large Files. Advanced Information Systems Division, Hughes Dynamics, Inc., Sherman Oaks, Calif., April 30, 1964.

Becker, Joseph, and Hayes, R. M. *Handbook of Data Processing for Libraries*. New York: John Wiley & Sons, 1970.

Booth, A. D. "On the Geometry of Libraries." *Journal of Documentation* 25 (March 1969): 28–40.

Booz, Allen, and Hamilton, Inc. *Problems in University Library Management*. A study conducted for the Association of Research Libraries and the American Council on Education. Washington, D.C.: Association of Research Libraries, 1970.

Bourne, C., and Densmore, G. *A Cost Analysis and Utilization Study of the Stanford University Library System*. Menlo Park, Calif.: Stanford Research Institute, 1969.

Bradford, S. C. *Documentation*. London: Lockwood, 1948.

Brookes, B. C. "Bradford's Law and the Bibliography of Science." *Nature*, December 6, 1966, pp. 953–56.

Brookes, B. C. "The Complete Bradford-Zipf 'Bibliograph.'" *Journal of Documentation* 25 (March 1969): 58–60.

Brookes, B. C. "The Derivation and Application of the Bradford-Zipf Distribution." *Journal of Documentation* 24 (December 1968): 247–65.

Brookes, B. C. "The Growth, Utility, and Obsolescence of Scientific Periodical Literature." *Journal of Documentation* 26 (December 1970): 283–94.

Brookes, B. C. "The Viability of Branch Libraries." *Journal of Librarianship* 2 (January 1970): 14–21.

Buckland, M. K., and Hindle, A. "Library Zipf." *Journal of Documentation* 25 (March 1969): 52–57.

Chamis, A. Y. "The Application of Computers at the B. F. Goodrich Research Center Library." *Special Libraries* 59 (January 1968): 24–29.

Cole, P. E. "Journal Usage versus Age of Journal." *Journal of Documentation* 19 (March 1963): 1–11.

Cox, J. G. *Optimum Storage of Library Materials.* Lafayette, Ind.: Purdue University Libraries, 1964.

Dougherty, R. M., and Heinritz, F. J. *Scientific Management of Library Operations.* Metuchen, N.J.: Scarecrow Press, 1966.

Duchesne, R. M. "Library Management Information from Computer-aided Library Systems." In *Planning Library Services: Proceedings of a Research Seminar Held at the University of Lancaster, 9–11 July 1969,* edited by A. G. MacKenzie and I. M. Stuart. Lancaster: University of Lancaster Library, 1969.

Ellsworth, Ralph E. *The Economics of Book Storage in College and University Libraries.* Metuchen, N.J.: Scarecrow Press, 1969.

Evans, G. E. "Book Selection and Book Collection Usage in Academic Libraries." *Library Quarterly* 40 (July 1970): 297–308.

Fussler, H. H., and Simon, J. L. *Patterns in the Use of Books in Large Research Libraries.* Chicago: University of Chicago Press, 1961.

Geiger, James W., and Trapp, R. E. *A Quantitative Analysis of the Management of Supply RCS Reports Controlled by Headquarters Air Force Logistics Command.* Wright-Patterson AFB, Ohio: Air Force Institute of Technology, 1963.

Gipson, John S. " 'Total Cost' of Acquisitions in a Community College." *College and Research Libraries* 28 (July 1967): 273–76.

Goffman, W., and Morris, T. G. "Bradford's Law and Library Acquisitions." *Nature,* June 6, 1970, pp. 922–23.

Goffman, W., and Warren, K. S. "Dispersion of Papers among Journals Based on a Mathematical Analysis of Two Diverse Medical Literatures." *Nature,* March 29, 1969, pp. 1205–7.

Groh, Kamil. "Za jednotny system vedecko-metodickeho rizeni knihoven" [Towards a unified system of scientific-methodological management of libraries]. *Knihovnik* 12 (1967): 101–5.

Gull, C. D. "Logical Flow Charts and Other New Techniques for the Administration of Libraries and Information Centers." *Library Resources and Technical Services* 12 (Winter 1968): 47–66.

Harvey, John, ed. *Data Processing in Public and University Libraries.* Washington, D.C.: Spartan Books, 1966.

Heilprin, L. R. "Response to Jesse H. Shera." In *The Foundations of Access to Knowledge,* edited by E. B. Montgomery. Syracuse, N.Y.: Division of Summer Sessions, Syracuse University, 1968.

Heinritz, F. J. "Quantitative Management in Libraries." *College and Research Libraries* 31 (July 1970): 232–38.

Herner, Saul, et al. *A Recommended Design for the United States Medical Library and Information System.* Washington, D.C.: Herner & Co., 1966.

Johns Hopkins University Library. *An Operations Research and Systems Engineering Study of a University Library.* Baltimore: Milton S. Eisenhower Library, Johns Hopkins University, 1968.

Kilgour, F. G. "Recorded Use of Books in the Yale Medical Library." *American Documentation* 12 (October 1961): 266–69.

Kilgour, F. G. "Use of Medical and Biological Journals in the Yale Medical Library." *Bulletin of the Medical Library Association* 50 (July 1962): 429–49.

Kurmey, William J. "Management Implications of Mechanization." In C.A.C.U.L. Workshop on Library Automation. *Automation in Libraries.* Ottawa: Canadian Association of College Libraries, 1967.

Lamkin, B. E. "Decision-making Tools for Improved Library Operations." *Special Libraries* 56 (November 1965): 642–46.

Lazorick, Gerald J. *Demand Models for Books in Library Circulation Systems.* Buffalo: School of Information and Library Studies, State University of New York at Buffalo, 1970.

Leimkuhler, F. F. "The Bradford Distribution." *Journal of Documentation* 23 (September 1967): 197–207.

Leimkuhler, F. F., and Cooper, M. D. *Analytical Planning for University Libraries.* Berkeley: University of California Press, 1970.

Leimkuhler, F. F., and Morelock, M. "Library Operations Research and Systems Engineering Studies." *College and Research Libraries* 25 (November 1964): 501–3.

Line, M. B. "The 'Half-Life' of Periodical Literature: Apparent and Real Obsolescence." *Journal of Documentation* 26 (March 1970): 46–54.

McGrath, W. E., and Barber, G. R. "An Allocation Formula Derived from a Factor Analysis of Academic Departments." *Col-*

lege and Research Libraries 30 (January 1969): 51–62.

Mackenzie, A. G., and Stuart, I. M., eds. *Planning Library Services. Proceedings of a Research Seminar Held at the University of Lancaster, 9–11 July 1969.* Lancaster: University of Lancaster Library, 1969.

Martyn, J. E. "Cost Effectiveness in Library Management." *Aslib Electronic Group Newsletter,* no. 40 (October 1969), pp. 3–9.

Merchant, H. D., and Sasieni, M. W. "Centralization or Decentralization of Case's Library Facilities." Paper read at Fourteenth National Meeting of the Operations Research Society of America, Saint Louis, Mo., October 23–24, 1958.

Momm, John Albert. *A Descriptive Programming Analysis of the Naval Postgraduate Textbook Library.* Monterey, Calif.: U.S. Naval Postgraduate School, 1969.

Morse, P. M. "Search Theory and Browsing." *Library Quarterly* 41 (October 1970): 391–408.

Mullick, S. K. "Optimal Design of a Stochastic System with Dominating Fixed Costs." Paper presented at TIMS, the Institute of Management Sciences, National Meeting, Dallas, Tex., February 16, 1966.

Newhouse, Joseph P. *Libraries and the Other Triangle under the Demand Curve.* Santa Monica, Calif.: RAND Corp., 1970.

Nistor, E., and Roman, E. "Despre conducerea stintifica a unitatilor de documentare" [Scientific management of documentation units]. *Probleme de informare si documentare* 3 (February 1969): 80–87.

Oh, Tai Keun. "New Dimensions of Management Theory." *College and Research Libraries* 27 (November 1966): 431–38.

Olson, E. E. "Quantitative Approaches to Assessment of Library Service Functions." In *Impact of Mechanization on Libraries: Fifth Annual Colloquium on Information Retrieval,* edited by James A. Ramey. Philadelphia: Information Interscience, Inc., 1968.

Piez, G. T. "Library Technology and RTSD—Goals in Common." *Library Resources and Technical Services* 10 (Winter 1966): 13–17.

Pings, Vern M. "Development of Quantitative Assessment of Medical Libraries." *College and Research Libraries* 29 (September 1968): 273–80.

Poage, Scott T. "Work Sampling in Library

Administration." *Library Quarterly* 30 (July 1960): 213–18.

Powers, Milton, and Tanis, N. E. "Profiles of Practice in the Public Junior College Library." *College and Research Libraries* 28 (September 1967): 331–36.

Roy, Robert H. *Progress Report on an Operations Research and Systems Engineering Study of a University Library.* Baltimore: Johns Hopkins University Library, 1965.

Saxena, S. K. "Compact Storage of Books in Open-Shelf Libraries Where Book Height Follows a Compound Type of Truncated Double Exponential Distribution." *Opsearch* 3 (1967): 157–67.

Schultheiss, Louis A.; Culbertson, Don S.; and Heiliger, Edward M. *Advanced Data Processing in the University Library.* Metuchen, N.J.: Scarecrow Press, 1962.

Shaw, R. R. "Scientific Management in the Library." *Wilson Library Bulletin* 21 (January 1947): 349–52.

Shaw, R. R., ed. "Scientific Management in Libraries." *Library Trends* 2 (January 1954): 359–60.

Taylor, Robert, and Hieber, C. E. *Manual for the Analysis of Library Systems.* Bethlehem, Pa.: Center for the Information Sciences, Lehigh University, 1965.

Thomas, P. A. "Tasks and the Analysis of Library Systems." *Aslib Proceedings* 22 (July 1970): 336–43.

Trueswell, R. W. "Determining the Optimum Number of Volumes for a Library's Holdings." Paper presented at the 1964 National Joint Meeting of the Institute of Management Sciences and Operations Research Society of America, Minneapolis, Minn., October 7–9, 1964.

Vij, V. P., and Christopher, M. "Cost/Benefit Analysis of Company Information Needs." *UNESCO Bulletin for Libraries* 24 (January-February 1970): 9–22.

MATHEMATICAL PROGRAMMING

Bellomy, F. L. "Management Planning for Library Systems Development." *Journal of Library Automation* 2 (December 1969): 187–217.

Chamis, Alice Y. "The Design of Information Systems: The Use of Systems Analysis." *Special Libraries* 60 (January 1969): 21–31.

Goyal, S. K. "Application of Operational Research to Problems of Determining Appropriate Loan Period for Periodicals." *Libri International* 20 (1970): 94–100.

Heinritz, Fred J. "Optimum Allocation of Technical Services Personnel." *Library Resources and Technical Services* 13 (Winter 1969): 99–101.

Konheim, A. G., and Weiss, B. "An Occupancy Discipline and Applications." *Siam Journal on Applied Mathematics* 14 (November 1966): 1266–74.

Leimkuhler, F. F., and Cox, J. Grady. "Compact Book Storage in Libraries." *Operations Research* 12 (May-June 1964): 419–27.

Lister, Winston C. *Least Cost Decision Rules for the Selection of Library Materials for Compact Storage.* Washington, D.C.: Office of Technical Services, 1967.

Morse, P. M. *Library Effectiveness: A Systems Approach.* Cambridge, Mass.: M.I.T. Press, 1968.

Müller, P. Heinz. "Die Bedeutung der Bedienungstheorie im Bibliothekswesen" [The impact of queueing theory on librarianship]. *Technische Universität Dresden, Wissenschaftliche Zeitschrift* 16 (1967): 1633–36.

MODELING

Andrews, Theodora. "The Role of Departmental Libraries in Operations Research Studies in a University Library." *Special Libraries* 59 (September 1968): 519–24 and 59 (October 1968): 638–44.

Arora, S. R., and Paul, R. N. "Acquisition of Library Materials: A Quantitative Approach." In *Proceedings of the Thirty-second Annual Meeting of the American Society for Information Science, San Francisco, October 1–4, 1969.* Vol. 6: *Cooperating Information Societies,* edited by J. B. North. Westport, Conn., and London: Greenwood Publishing Corp., 1969.

Brookes, B. C. "Obsolescence of Special Library Periodicals: Sampling Errors and Utility Contours." *Journal of the American Society for Information Science* 21 (September 1970): 320–29.

Buckland, M. K., and Hindle, A. "Loan Policies, Duplication and Availability." In *Planning Library Services: Proceedings of a Research Seminar Held at the University of Lancaster, 9–11 July, 1969,* edited by A. G. Mackenzie and I. M. Stuart. Lancaster: University of Lancaster Library, 1969.

Buckland, M. K., and Woodburn, I. "An Analytical Approach to Duplication and Availability." *University of Lancaster Occasional Papers,* no. 2. Lancaster: University of Lancaster Library, 1968.

Bush, G. C. "Attendance and Use of the Science Library at M.I.T." *American Documentation* 7 (April 1956): 87–109.

Clapp, Verner, and Jordan, Robert. *Quantitative Criteria for Adequacy for Library Holdings.* Washington, D.C.: Council on Library Resources, 1965.

Dunn, O. C.; Seibert, W. F.; and Scheuneman, J. A. *The Past and Likely Future of 58 Research Libraries, 1951–1980: A Statistical Study of Growth and Change.* Lafayette, Ind.: Universities Libraries and Audio Visual Center, Purdue University, 1965.

Dynin, I. M. "Analiz informatsionnykh sistem na osnove teorii avtomaticheskogo upravleniya" [The analysis of information systems on the basis of automatic control theory]. *Nauchno-Tekhnickeskaya Informatsiya,* 2d ser. (1969), pp. 29–34.

Gurk, H. M. "Storage Requirements for Information Handling Centres." *Journal of the Association for Computing Machinery* 17 (January 1970): 65–77.

Hayes, Robert M. *Project Status: An Approach to Methodology (Criteria and Goals for the Libraries of the University of California).* Los Angeles: Institute of Library Research, 1966.

Jain, A. K. "Sampling and Short-Period Usage in the Purdue Library." *College and Research Libraries* 27 (May 1966): 211–18.

La Zorick, G. J. "Use of Monte Carlo Methods to Determine File Maintenance Criteria for an Automated Library Acquisition System." Paper presented at the Thirteenth National Meeting, Operations Research Society of America, Durham, N.C., October 17–19, 1966.

Leimkuhler, F. F. "Library Operations Research: An Engineering Approach to Information Problems." *Engineering Education* 60 (January 1970): 363–65.

Leimkuhler, F. F. "A Literature Search and File Organization Model." *American Documentation* 19 (April 1968): 131–36.

Leimkuhler, F. F. "Mathematical Models for Library Systems Analysis." *Drexel Library Quarterly* 4 (July 1968) 185–96.

Leimkuhler, F. F. "On Information Storage Models." In *Planning Library Services:*

Proceedings of a Research Seminar Held at the University of Lancaster, 9–11 July 1969, edited by A. G. Mackenzie and I. M. Stuart. Lancaster: University of Lancaster Library, 1969.

Leimkuhler, F. F. "Operations Research in the Purdue Libraries." In *Automation in the Library—When, Where, and How,* edited by Theodora Andrews. Lafayette, Ind.: Purdue University, 1964.

Leimkuhler, F. F. "Systems Analysis in University Libraries." *College and Research Libraries* 27 (January 1966): 13–18.

Leimkuhler, F. F.; Jain, A. K.; and Anderson, V. L. "A Statistical Model of Book Use and Its Application to the Book Storage Problem." *American Statistical Association Journal* 64 (December 1969): 1211–24.

Liban, F. B. "A New, Generalized Model for Information-Transfer: A Systems Approach." *American Documentation* 20 (October 1969): 381–84.

Mackenzie, A. G. "Bibliotheconomics: Or, Library Science Revised." *An Leabharlann* 28 (September 1970): 97–105.

Martyn, J., and Vickery, B. C. "The Complexity of the Modelling of Information Systems." *Journal of Documentation* 26 (September 1970): 204–20.

Meise, Norman R. *Conceptual Design of an Automated National Library System.* Metuchen, N.J.: Scarecrow Press, 1969.

Morse, P. M. "Probabilistic Models for Library Operations." Minutes of Sixty-third Meeting, Association of Research Libraries, Chicago, January 1964.

Morse, Philip M., and Elston, Caroline. "A Probabilistic Model for Obsolescence." *Operations Research* 17 (January-February 1969): 36–47.

Muller, R. H. "Economics of Compact Book Shelving." *Library Trends* 13 (April 1965): 433–47.

Nance, R. E. "An Analytical Model of a Library Network." *Journal of the American Society for Information Science* 21 (January-February 1970): 58–66.

Nance, R. E. "Strategic Simulation of a Library-User-Funder System." Ph.D. dissertation, Purdue University, 1967.

National Advisory Commission on Libraries. *On the Economics of Library Operation.* Princeton, N.J.: Mathematica, 1967.

Neuman, K., and Riedel, H. "Über die Modellierung von Struktur and Informa-

tionsfluss des betrieblichen Informationssystem Wissenschaft mit Technik mit Hilfe einer Kreisdarstellung" [Modeling the structure and information flow of an industrial information system using a circular flow diagram]. *Informatik* 16 (1969): 32–36.

Nitecki, J. Z. "Towards a Conceptual Pattern in Librarianship: A Model." *General Systems Bulletin* 2 (June 1970): 2–16.

Raffel, L. J. *Compact Book Storage Models.* Lafayette, Ind.: Purdue University, 1965.

Reichard, E. W., and Orsagh, T. J. "Holdings and Expenditures of U.S. Academic Libraries: An Evaluative Technique." *College and Research Libraries* 27 (November 1966): 478–87.

Rider, Fremont. *The Scholar and the Future of the Research Library.* New York: Hadham Press, 1944.

Stephens, I. E. "Computer Simulation of Library Operations: An Evaluation of an Administrative Tool." *Special Libraries* 61 (July-August 1970): 280–87.

Surace, Cecily, J. *Library Circulation Systems: An Overview.* Santa Monica, Calif.: RAND Corp., 1970.

Thomas, P. A. "A Procedural Model for the Use of Bibliographic Records in Libraries." *Aslib Occasional Publication No. 4.* London: Aslib, 1970.

Trueswell, Richard W. "A Quantitative Measure of User Circulation Requirements and Its Possible Effect on Stack Thinning and Multiple Copy Determination." *American Documentation* 16 (January 1965): 20–25.

University of Lancaster. *Report of the Librarian for 1969–1970.* Lancaster: University of Lancaster Library, 1970.

Woodburn, I. "A Mathematical Model of a Hierarchial Library System." In *Planning Library Services: Proceedings of a Research Seminar Held at the University of Lancaster, 9–11 July 1969,* edited by A. G. Mackenzie and I. M. Stuart. Lancaster: University of Lancaster Library, 1969.

SYSTEMS ANALYSIS

Adelson, Marvin. "The System Approach: A Perspective." *Wilson Library Bulletin* 42 (March 1968): 711–15.

ASLIB Research Department. "The Analysis of Library Processes." *Journal of Documentation* 26 (March 1970): 30–45.

Bellomy, F. L. "The Systems Approach Solves

Library Problems." *ALA Bulletin* 62 (October 1968): 1121–25.

Buckland, M. K.; Hindle, A.; McKenzie, A. G.; and Woodburn, I. "Systems Analysis of a University Library: Final Report on a Research Project." *University of Lancaster Library Occasional Papers,* no. 4. Lancaster: University of Lancaster Library, 1970.

Burkhalter, B. R., ed. *Case Studies in Systems Analysis in a University Library.* Metuchen, N.J.: Scarecrow Press, 1968.

Chapman, E. A., and St. Pierre, P. L., *Systems Analysis and Design as Related to Library Operations.* A Manual for a Symposium Sponsored by the Upstate New York Chapter, Special Libraries Association, Saratoga Springs, New York. London: John Wiley & Sons, 1967.

Chapman, E. A.; St. Pierre, Paul L.; and Lubans, John, Jr. *Library Systems Analysis Guidelines.* New York: John Wiley & Sons, 1970.

Covill, G. W. "Librarian + Systems Analyst = Teamwork?" *Special Libraries* 58 (February 1967): 99–101.

Duggan, M. "Library Network Analysis and Planning." *Journal of Library Automation* 2 (September 1969): 157–75.

Fasana, P. J. "Determining the Cost of Library Automation." *ALA Bulletin* 61 (June 1967): 656–61.

Flood, M. M. "The Systems Approach to Library Planning." *Library Quarterly* 34 (October 1964): 326–38.

Gordon, P. J. "All Very Well in Practice! But How Does It in Theory?" *Wilson Library Bulletin* 42 (March 1968): 676–85.

Graziano. E. E. " 'Machine-Men' and Librarians, an Essay." *College and Research Libraries* 28 (November 1967): 403–6.

Hamburg, M.; Clelland, Richard C.; Bommer, Michael R. W.; Ramist, Leonard E.; and Whitfield, Ronald M. "A Systems Analysis of the Library and Information Science Statistical Data System: The Research." Interim report. 2 vols. Philadelphia: University of Pennsylvania, Wharton School of Finance and Commerce, 1970.

Hayes, Robert. "Library Systems Analysis." In *Data Processing in Public and University Libraries,* edited by John Harvey. Washington, D.C.: Spartan Books, 1966.

Herner, Saul. "Systems Design, Evaluation and Costing." *Special Libraries* 58 (October 1967): 576–81.

Jestes, E. C. "An Example of Systems Analysis: Locating a Book in a Reference Room." *Special Libraries* 59 (November 1968): 722–28.

Kemper, R. E. "Strategic Planning for Library Systems." Seattle: University of Washington, 1968.

Kilgour, F. G., "Systems Concepts and Libraries." *College and Research Libraries* 28 (May 1967): 167–70.

Lamkin, B. E. "Integrated Library Management and Systems Concepts." In *American Documentation Institute, Proceedings.* Vol. 1: *Parameters of Information Science,* edited by A. W. Elias. Washington, D.C.: Thompson Book Co., 1964.

Lamkin, B. E. "Systems Analysis in Top Management Communication." *Special Libraries* 58 (February 1967): 90–94.

Leimkuhler, F. F. "Planning University Library Services: An Overview." In *Planning Library Services: Proceedings of a Research Seminar Held at the University of Lancaster, 9–11 July 1969,* edited by A. G. Mackenzie and I. M. Stuart. Lancaster: University of Lancaster Library, 1969.

Liston, D. M., and Schoene, M. L. "A Systems Approach to the Design of Information Systems." *Journal of the American Society for Information Science* 22 (March 1971): 115–22.

Mackenzie, A. G. "Systems Analysis of a University Library." *Program* 2 (April 1968): 7–14.

Mackenzie, A. G. "Systems Analysis of a University Library." In *Library Systems and Information Services: Proceedings of the Second Anglo-Czech Conference of Information Specialists,* edited by D. J. Foskett, Ade Reuck, and H. Coblans. London: Crosby Lockwood, 1970.

Markuson, B. E. "Systems Implications of Interlibrary Cooperation." *Pacific Northwest Library Association Quarterly* 33 (January 1969): 4–13.

Martyn, J. "Evaluation of Information-Handling Systems." *Aslib Proceedings* 21 (August 1969): 317–24.

Minder, Thomas. "Library Systems Analyst: A Job Description." *College and Research Libraries* 27 (July 1966): 271–76.

Moore, Edythe. "Systems Analysis: An Overview." *Special Libraries* 58 (February 1967) : 87–90.

Nance, Richard E. "Systems Analysis and the Study of Information Systems." In *American Documentation Institute, Proceedings.* Washington, D.C.: Thompson Book Co., 1967.

Parker, T. F. "Missing Stream: Operations Management in Libraries." *Library Journal* 94 (January 1969): 42–43.

Raffel, J. A., and Shishko, R. *Systematic Analysis of University Libraries: An Application of Cost-Benefit Analysis to the M.I.T. Libraries.* Cambridge, Mass.: M.I.T. Press, 1969.

Raphael, D. L. "Systems Concepts and the Library." In *Administration and Change: Continuing Education in Library Adminis-* *tration.* New Brunswick, N.J.: Rutgers University Press, 1969.

Richmond, Phyllis A. "Systems Evaluation by Comparison Testing." *College and Research Libraries* 27 (January 1966) : 23–30.

Robinson, F. *Systems Analysis in Libraries.* Newcastle upon Tyne: Oriel Press, 1969.

Schultheiss, Louis A. "Systems Analysis and Planning." In *Data Processing and University Libraries,* edited by John Harvey. Washington, D.C.: Spartan Books, 1966.

Shera, Jesse H. "An Epistemological Foundation for Library Science." In *The Foundations of Access to Knowledge,* edited by E. B. Montgomery. Syracuse, N.Y.: Division of Summer Sessions, Syracuse University, 1968.

THE CONTRIBUTORS

U. NARAYAN BHAT: professor of computer science and operations research, Southern Methodist University. Born 1933, Vittal, India. B.A. in mathematics, 1953; B.T. in education, 1954, University of Madras; M.A. in statistics, 1958, Karnatak University; Ph.D. in mathematics, 1964, University of Western Australia. Author of twenty-seven papers and monographs on queueing and traffic flow theory, time-sharing systems, applied probability, and stochastic processes.

MICHAEL R. W. BOMMER: assistant professor of statistics and operations research, Temple University. Born 1940, Batavia, New York. B.S. in mechanical engineering, 1963, Cornell University; M.S. in industrial engineering, 1964, Ohio State University; Ph.D. in statistics, 1971, University of Pennsylvania. Coauthor of *A Systems Analysis of the Library and Information Science Statistical Data System: The Preliminary Study* (U.S. Department of Health, Education, and Welfare, Office of Education, 1969).

ABRAHAM BOOKSTEIN: assistant professor, Graduate Library School, University of Chicago. Born 1940, New York City. B.S., 1961, City College of New York; M.S., 1966, University of California, Berkeley; Ph.D., 1969, Yeshiva University; M.A. in library science, 1970, University of Chicago. Coeditor of "Operations Research: Implications for Libraries" with Don R. Swanson.

MICHAEL K. BUCKLAND: assistant librarian for research, University of Lancaster, England. Born 1941, Wantage, England. M.A., 1963, Oxford University; Postgraduate diploma in librarianship, 1965, Sheffield University. Author of Occasional Papers issued by the University of Lancaster, for example, *Some Implications for Library Management of Scattering and Obsolescence* (1968) and *Systems Analysis of a University Library* (1970). Also author of numerous journal articles on various aspects of the scientific management of libraries.

C. WEST CHURCHMAN: research philosopher, Space Sciences Laboratory, University of California, Berkeley. Born 1913, Philadelphia, Pennsylvania. A.B., 1935; M.A., 1936; Ph.D., 1938, University of Pennsylvania. Author of many articles published in *Operations Research, Management Science,* and *Philosophy of Science.* Along with Russell L. Ackoff and E. Leonard Arnoff, he published one of the first introductory texts in operations research entitled *Introduction to Operations Research* (Wiley, 1957). Subsequently, he has written two prize-winning books on management and is currently writing *On the Design of Inquiring Systems,* to be published by Basic Books in 1971.

FRED W. GLOVER: professor, Department of Management Science, School of Business, University of Colorado. Born 1937, Kansas City, Missouri. B.B.A. in accounting, 1960, University of Missouri, Kansas City; Ph.D. in operations research, 1965, Carnegie-Mellon University. Author of forty research reports and more than twenty-five publications appearing in journals and books on management science and operations research.

MORRIS HAMBURG: professor of statistics and operations research, Wharton School, University of Pennsylvania. Born 1922, Philadelphia, Pennsylvania. A.B., 1943; A.M., 1948; Ph.D. in economics, 1952, University of Pennsylvania. Author of *Statistical Decision Theory and Benefit-Cost Analysis for Preferredness of Choice among Alternative Projects* (Lund, 1967) and coauthor of *Computer Model for New Product Demand* (Harvard Business Research, March, 1967).

DARWIN KLINGMAN: assistant professor of business, University of Texas. Born 1944, Dickinson, North Dakota. B.A. in mathematics, 1966; M.A. in mathematics, 1967, Washington State University; Ph.D. in mathematics-computer science-business administration, 1969, University of Texas. Author or coauthor of numerous articles about the distribution model.

MANFRED KOCHEN: professor of information science and urban regional planning, and research mathematician, Mental Health Research Institute, University of Michigan. Born 1928, Vienna, Austria. B.S., 1950, Massachusetts Institute of Technology; M.A., 1951; Ph.D. in applied mathematics, 1955, Columbia University. Author of *Some Problems in Information Science* (Scarecrow Press, 1965) and compiler of *The Growth of Knowledge: Readings on Organization and Retrieval of Information* (Wiley, 1967).

ROBERT R. KORFHAGE: director, Computer Sciences/Operations Research Center, Southern Methodist University. Born 1930, Syracuse, New York. B.S.E. in mathematics, 1952; M.S., 1955; Ph.D. in mathematics, 1962, University of Michigan. Author of *Logic and Algorithms, with Applications to the Computer and Information Sciences* (Wiley, 1966) and coauthor of *Calculus* (Academic Press, 1970).

FERDINAND F. LEIMKUHLER: professor and head, School of Industrial Engineering, Purdue University. Born 1928, Baltimore, Maryland. B.S., 1950, Loyola College, Maryland; B.Eng., 1952; Dr.Eng., 1962, Johns Hopkins University. Director of the extensive study involving research and systems analysis of Purdue University's main library as a facilities laboratory for students.

BEN-AMI LIPETZ: head, Research Department, Yale University Library. Born 1927, Fargo, North Dakota. B.M.E., 1948; Ph.D., 1959, Cornell University. Author of *The Measurement of Efficiency of Scientific Research* (Intermedia, 1965), *A Guide to Case Studies of Scientific Activity* (Intermedia, 1965), and many journal articles on information storage and retrieval.

PHILIP M. MORSE: professor of physics, Operations Research Center, Massachusetts Institute of Technology. Born 1903, Shreveport, Louisiana. B.S., 1926, Case Institute of Technology; M.A., 1927; Ph.D., 1929, Princeton University. Author of *Quantum Mechanics* (McGraw-Hill, 1930), *Methods of Operations Research* (M.I.T. Press, 1936), *Methods of Theoretical Physics* (McGraw-Hill, 1953), *Library Effectiveness* (M.I.T. Press, 1968), and

other books on physics, acoustics, operations research, and their application.

RICHARD E. NANCE: associate professor of computer science and operations research, Southern Methodist University. B.S.I.E., 1962; M.S.I.E., 1966, North Carolina State University; Ph.D., 1968, Purdue University. Author of fifteen papers and monographs on digital simulation, queueing theory, information systems, and information retrieval.

LEONARD RAMIST: research associate, Department of Statistics and Operations Research, Wharton School, University of Pennsylvania. Born 1942, New York City. B.S. in economics, 1962; M.S. in operations research, 1968, University of Pennsylvania. Graduate courses completed for Ph.D., University of Pennsylvania. Coauthor of *A Systems Analysis of the Library and Information Science Statistical Data System: The Preliminary Study* (U.S. Department of Health, Education, and Welfare, Office of Education, 1969).

VLADIMIR SLAMECKA: professor and director, School of Information and Computer Sciences, Georgia Institute of Technology. Born 1928, Brno, Czechoslovakia. Attended Brno School of Technology, 1947–49; University of Sydney, 1951–53; University of Munich, 1953–55; M.S., 1958; D.L.S., 1962, Columbia University. Author or editor of five monographs and forty papers, and a holder of several patents.

DON R. SWANSON: dean, Graduate Library School, University of Chicago. Born 1924, Los Angeles, California. B.S., 1945, California Institute of Technology; M.A., 1947, Rice University; Ph.D., 1952, University of California. Author of "Searching Natural Language Text by Computer," *Science* (October 21, 1960); "Interrogating a Computer in Natural Language," *Information Processing*, vol. 62 (North-Holland Publishing Co., 1963); "Dialogues with a Catalog," *Library Quarterly*, vol. 34 (January 1964); and "Some Unexplained Aspects of the Cranfield Tests of Indexing Performance Factors," *Library Quarterly*, vol. 41 (July 1971).